LEE PRESTON

7D Gleneagles court

Ardler

DUNDEE

DD2 36U

FROM THE 30s TO THE 70s

Introduction by
E. NELSON BRIDWELL
Editor and Writer of <u>Batman</u> newspaper strip

SPRING BOOKS
London · New York · Sydney · Toronto

SPECIAL COVER CREDITS

EXCEPT AS OTHERWISE NOTED ALL COVERS ARE FROM BATMAN COMICS

PAGE #	VOL. #	NOTICE	PAGE #	VOL. #	NOTICE
18-19	Batman 9	© 1941 Detective Comics, Inc. Renewed 1969 by National Periodical Publications, Inc.	113		© 1957 National Comics Publications, Inc.
	11	© 1942 Detective Comics, Inc. Renewed 1969 by National Periodical Publications, Inc.	118		© 1958 National Comics Publications, Inc.
	17	© 1943 Detective Comics, Inc. Renewed 1971 by National Periodical Publications, Inc.	231-232	Batman 128	© 1959 National Comics Publications, Inc.
	20	© 1943 Detective Comics, Inc. Renewed 1971 by National Periodical Publications, Inc.	129		© 1959 National Comics Publications, Inc.
	37	© 1946 Detective Comics, Inc.	146		© 1962 National Periodical Publications, Inc.
	50	© 1948 National Comics Publications, Inc.	156		© 1963 National Periodical Publications, Inc.
	Detective 27	© 1939 Detective Comics, Inc. Renewed 1966 by National Periodical Publications, Inc.	165		© 1964 National Periodical Publications, Inc.
	31	© 1939 Detective Comics, Inc. Renewed 1966 by National Periodical Publications, Inc.	168		© 1964 National Periodical Publications, Inc.
	33	© 1939 Detective Comics, Inc. Renewed 1966 by National Periodical Publications, Inc.	175		© 1965 National Periodical Publications, Inc.
	37	© 1940 Detective Comics, Inc. Renewed 1967 by National Periodical Publications, Inc.	184		© 1966 National Periodical Publications, Inc.
	38	© 1940 Detective Comics, Inc. Renewed 1967 by National Periodical Publications, Inc.	192		© 1967 National Periodical Publications, Inc.
			194		© 1967 National Periodical Publications, Inc.
	120	© 1946 National Comics Publications, Inc.	200		© 1968 National Periodical Publications, Inc.
125-126	Batman 57	© 1949 National Comics Publications, Inc.	205		© 1968 National Periodical Publications, Inc.
	59	© 1950 National Comics Publications, Inc.	297-298	Batman 227	© 1970 National Periodical Publications, Inc.
	63	© 1950 National Comics Publications, Inc.	230		© 1971 National Periodical Publications, Inc.
	67	© 1951 National Comics Publications, Inc.	231		© 1971 National Periodical Publications, Inc.
	68	© 1951 National Comics Publications, Inc.	232		© 1971 National Periodical Publications, Inc.
	72	© 1952 National Comics Publications, Inc.	234		© 1971 National Periodical Publications, Inc.
	78	© 1953 National Comics Publications, Inc.		Detective 395	© 1969 National Periodical Publications, Inc.
	83	© 1954 National Comics Publications, Inc.	397		© 1970 National Periodical Publications, Inc.
	87	© 1954 National Comics Publications, Inc.	399		© 1970 National Periodical Publications, Inc.
	109	© 1957 National Comics Publications, Inc.	400		© 1970 National Periodical Publications, Inc.
			402		© 1970 National Periodical Publications, Inc.
			403		© 1970 National Periodical Publications, Inc.
			413		© 1971 National Periodical Publications, Inc.

Published by arrangement with Crown Publishers, Inc., New York by
The Hamlyn Publishing Group Limited
London · New York · Sydney · Toronto
Hamlyn House, Feltham, Middlesex, England
First Impression 1972
ISBN 0 600 31303 4

Printed in England by Jarrold & Sons Ltd., Norwich

DEDICATION

BATMAN! It was your first public appearance some forty years ago that changed the life of a young shoeshine boy into the artist that drew you, then into the editor that directed you, and finally your publisher.

My sincerest thanks for a lifetime career that has surpassed anything my imagination could have conceived.

Carmine Infantino

CARMINE INFANTINO
PUBLISHER

TABLE OF CONTENTS

COLOR SECTIONS

INTRODUCTION

by

E. Nelson Bridwell

I don't remember the date . . . or the exact year . . . of that fantastic occurrence. I know I was a fan of the "Superman" radio show, and on this particular day Superman found a wounded boy in a drifting rowboat—a boy clad in a red vest and yellow cape.

It was, of course, Robin, the Boy Wonder!

And thus began the fabulous Superman-Batman team.

Somehow, the two heroes seemed destined to wind up working together. Yet, at that time—in the mid-forties—they had never really done so. True, they'd been regulars in *World's Finest Comics* since its inception, but, though the two (and Robin) were featured together on the covers, they starred in separate stories inside. Both were honorary members of the Justice Society of America, but so far they had made only a brief appearance with that hero group (in *All Star Comics*), popping in for a couple of panels.

Now, on radio, the team had finally been born. Soon, Batman and Superman knew each other's identities (though Robin did not then share in the knowledge that the Man of Steel was Clark Kent), and they often helped each other ward off identity-seekers. One actor who played Batman was Gary Merrill.

9

INTRODUCTION

Not until the fifties would Superman and Batman again team up. But that will have to wait. I have first to tell you of the origin of the Caped Crime-fighter.

Detective Comics had brought a new concept to comics in 1937. Prior to that time, comic books had been largely confined to reprints from the newspaper strips. *Detective* came up with all-new features—and all geared in one direction—*detection!* The magazine was successful, but boasted no really big guns. Then, in 1938, DC (named for *Detective Comics*) brought out *Action Comics*, which changed the comics world again, with Superman.

A new craze hit comics now—superheroes. Either the hero had fantastic powers, or he wore a colorful, circus costume—or both (I should say, *usually* both). One of the first of the new crimebusters, and the most durable after Superman himself, was The Batman.

Notice that this time I said *The* Batman. It was the usual way of referring to him at the time. Then he was a mysterious figure of the night. Later, when he became more of a public character, he was just good ol' Batman. Only recently has the article been restored, as the strange creature of darkness has been reborn.

Just where did The Batman come from? True, he wore a skintight costume, like Superman's—except that The Batman wore a cowl, and his cape resembled batwings. True, he, too, had a secret identity—and he fought crime. But there were vast differences.

For one thing, The Batman had no superpowers. He relied on his superb athletic skill, his cunning, and the terror he instilled in criminals to carry him through. And his costume, unlike most, was somber, designed to blend in with the night.

Secret identities were, after all, nothing new. The Scarlet Pimpernel had been Sir Percy Blakeney, darling of society, in Baroness Orczy's books. El Zorro had been Don Diego Vega, wealthy young poet, in Johnston McCulley's tales. There had even been a Romberg operetta *The Desert Song*, which concerned Pierre Birabeau, son of a general, who, disguised as The Red Shadow, led the Riffs in revolt against his own father. The Batman certainly followed this tradition, with his secret identity of playboy Bruce Wayne.

It is notable that the first actor to portray Zorro on the screen was Douglas

Fairbanks, Sr. For Fairbanks was one of the inspirations for The Batman, as Bob Kane, the Masked Manhunter's creator, has often stated. It was this movie hero's derring-do that was responsible for Kane's creation's becoming an "acro-Batman."

The Shadow was another hero of Kane's, and he contributed the image of a cloaked avenger, slipping through the shadows of a great city at night. But aside from his cloak and slouch hat, The Shadow had always dressed like any other man. The Batman took his costume not only from the Superman image, but also from the villain in a movie version of Mary Roberts Rinehart's *The Bat*, made in 1926. This awesome bat costume stuck in Kane's mind and was eventually transferred to his hero.

But The Batman is more than all these. He is a first-rate detective and escape artist. He is, in short, The Scarlet Pimpernel, Zorro, Fairbanks, The Shadow, The Bat, Sherlock Holmes, and Houdini, all rolled into one.

And his name was Bruce Wayne—strikingly similar to the name of the young man who created him. Wish fulfillment? Kane admits as much. The Batman was what he'd like to be; he rightly guessed that others would feel the same.

Today The Batman works hand in hand with the law; but it was not always the case. Look at the first story in this book and you will see him being hunted by the police, who resented this mystery man's taking the law into his own hands. And he did it—in quite striking ways. More than one murderer was done away with by the Cowled Crimebuster in those early days. But that was the tradition of the times. Many a superhero killed with no compunction if he felt the victim deserved it. No fooling around with habeas corpus or trial by jury or the fifth amendment. The heroes dealt out their own brand of justice quickly and efficiently. No wonder they needed secret identities!

But time went on and The Batman became more of a public figure—especially after the addition of Robin. How can a man go creeping around, blending with the shadows, when he has a kid in a red, yellow, and green costume trailing along behind him? In retrospect, it seems an unlikely combination—yet it worked!

Whence Robin? Actually, the idea of a boy fighting alongside an adult hero was nothing new in children's literature. It had even entered the area of the comic strip—notably in Caniff's *Dickie Dare* and *Terry and the Pirates*. But in all these cases, the kid was the main character. Here, Robin was added as an afterthought, a year after The Batman made his debut. His name and his costume were inspired by Robin Hood. To Bob Kane, he seemed a natural—a hero the kids could identify with. It was the wish fulfillment of Kane's childhood, as The Batman was the wish fulfillment of his teen years.

(I might add here that, despite the resemblance of the name to his creator's, Bruce Wayne is said to be taken from Robert the Bruce, the heroic Scottish king, and "Mad" Anthony Wayne, the Revolutionary War hero.)

In planning Robin's debut (which appears on page 64), a careful plot was worked out which would make him a natural as The Batman's aide. He needed acrobatic training, so he was made an aerialist in a circus. His parents having been killed, Bruce Wayne took him in—thus the team was formed.

The idea was a hit. It was widely copied, with The Shield and Dusty, Captain America and Bucky, The Green Arrow and Speedy, The Wizard and Roy, T.N.T. and Dan the Dyna-Mite, The Sandman and Sandy—and so on. There was even the ultimate switch—the Star-Spangled Kid, a teen-age hero, and his adult aide Stripesy. One thing was a bit puzzling. Why was it that the kid always had to be the ward of his partner? This had been necessary in the case of The Batman and Robin because Bruce's life had been pretty well sketched out, and he had no son or kid brother. Why was this always slavishly followed? Who knows?

I would like now to deal with one of the most irresponsible slurs ever cast upon our heroes. A certain psychiatrist decided that a man and a boy living together spelled homosexuality. Unfortunately, many people eagerly seized on this view—especially the gay set themselves. Today, when a comedian calls someone Bruce, you can almost bet he means the guy is a swishy character. Yet nothing could be further from the truth.

Other heroes have *a* girl friend. Not so with Bruce Wayne. When I say he's a playboy, I mean it. There was Julie Madison, who was his fiancée for a time before and after Robin came on the scene. She was succeeded by Linda Page, a society girl who turned to nursing to be of some service to the world. Then came Vicki Vale, news photographer, in the late forties (a too-obvious copy of Lois Lane), who was continually trying to ferret out The Batman's secret identity. Next, The Batwoman appeared—like Robin an ex-circus star. (So why was The Batman the one who spotted the fact that she spoke circus slang, when Robin should have caught on at once? Probably a scripting job with insufficient research.) Vicki and The Batwoman were rivals for The Batman for a time. When they faded, anything like a permanent romance faded, too. There have been plenty of girls, but obviously, Bruce doesn't hanker to be tied down to any *one* female. Batgirl has a beau of her own now, and any girl who really catches the Caped Crusader's eye generally fades like the phantom female in "The Demon of Gothos Mansion"—the last story in this book.

Heretofore, I have referred only to Bob Kane; yet he was but one of the many persons whose creative talent went to make up the Batman Legend. With The Batman appearing in *Detective Comics, World's Finest Comics,* and *Batman,* as well as a newspaper strip which started in 1943, he couldn't even do all the artwork. Jerry Robinson, Mort Meskin, Dick Sprang, Carmine Infantino, Win Mortimer, and Jim Mooney were some of the many artists who drew The Batman from time to time—although Bob Kane, as the creator, always had his name on it.

And Kane did not write the stories, though he often had a hand in creating the characters in them. One of the chief writers of The Batman for many years—in fact, *the* chief one—was Bill Finger. One sure sign of a Finger script was the presence of gigantic working models of everyday objects. They might be outdoor signs or indoor displays, but they were exact replicas of their smaller originals. His giant sewing machines really sewed; his giant phonographs played; and his giant paint tubes were chock full of real paint, ready to squirt in the Joker's face.

The Joker! Of all the villains The Batman has ever faced, this is the greatest. He is the perfect blend of clownish humor and malevolent evil. I have heard Bill Finger tell just how the character came to be created. It seems Bill got a call from Bob Kane. He had an idea for a villain Bill could use in the comics. He was a clownish-looking man, but a killer. However, when Bill saw Bob's sketch, he decided it looked *too* clownish. He happened to have a movie edition of Victor Hugo's *The Man Who Laughs,* with stills from the 1928 film starring Conrad Veidt. The story concerns Gwynplaine, an English nobleman stolen as an infant and turned into a carnival freak by having a perpetual laugh carved on his face. The makeup used by Veidt was perfect, and this inspired the Joker's grinning countenance.

Other villains quickly followed, including the Penguin, the Catwoman (who started as a "plainclothes" jewel thief called The Cat), Tweedledum and Tweedledee, Punch and Judy, and Two-Face. This last was probably one of the best villains ever created. His name was Harvey Kent in the first stories, but was later changed to Dent, probably because of The Batman's buddy

Clark Kent. Originally, there were but three Two-Face stories, ending with Kent submitting to plastic surgery, serving time in prison, and then reforming. There was a different Two-Face in the newspaper strip. In this one, he was not a district attorney, but an actor—and he ended by falling, catching his neck in some wires, and being hanged. The magazines had at least two fake Two-Faces (one of whom is in this book) before the original suffered an accident that restored his hideous countenance (another tale in this volume). Recently, Two-Face has come back to bedevil The Batman (in *Batman* #234).

The Riddler appeared briefly—but in only two stories in the forties. He was destined for revival much later. The Scarecrow was another early Batman villain who has been brought back in recent years.

Besides appearing on radio with Superman, The Batman and Robin also starred in two movie serials. The first, titled simply *Batman*, had a few disappointments for purists—since Lewis Wilson wore a costume somewhat less than skintight (no real outfit could match those in the comics, which looked like they'd been painted on). Also, the ears on his cowl looked too much like a devil's horns. Still, he and Douglas Croft (as Robin) did well enough in this 1943 Columbia production. And the actor who portrayed their butler Alfred was perfect. However, I've heard it said that Alfred lost weight and grew a moustache in the comics to resemble his screen version. That may be true—still, it was nice to have an Alfred who did *not* look like Arthur Treacher. The main fault of the picture, however, was the blatant racism with which it attacked the Japanese. Not only was J. Carroll Naish, as Dr. Daka, incredibly villainous, but the narration applauded the internment of Nisei by the U.S. government on the stated grounds that *all* Japs were devils. When the picture was rereleased as a feature in the sixties, this stood out terribly.

The Dynamic Duo had one more screen appearance before the decade ended—in another Columbia serial, *Batman and Robin*. I haven't seen it myself, but those who have report it was more filled with scientific gadgetry than the first.

As the forties faded and the fifties flew in, comic books were changing. The costumed heroes were dropping like flies in favor of everything from romance to horror. Even Wonder Woman lost two of the three magazines in which she had regularly appeared. Only two heroes had the stamina to keep going during that period—Superman and The Batman. Aquaman and The Green Arrow hung on—but only because they were backup features in magazines that starred the Man of Steel and the Gotham Goliath. Both had, from the first issue, been starred in *World's Finest Comics*. They had finally teamed in a lead story in *Superman*. (*See* the *Superman* book, published by Crown, for this story.) Now, when *World's Finest* was reduced in both pages and price, the two heroes began to star in a series of adventures as a team. This time, unlike the radio series, Robin was let in on Superman's secret identity. Some of the Superman-Batman series are included in this volume.

The fifties brought many additions to the Batman family. There was The Batwoman, The Bat-Hound, and even Bat-Mite, a magical being from another dimension who hero-worshiped The Batman. The worst feature of the late fifties was turning Batman into a science-fiction feature, complete with space travel and creatures of all sorts. This went over okay in *World's Finest*, with Superman, who had always been an s-f character—but without him, Batman and Robin (that "The" had largely been dropped by this time) were out of their element. Since the forties, they had been taking time trips through hypnosis; now, they were using a conventional time machine.

Batman's image remained unchanged from this at the start of the sixties, and things became more complicated with the introduction of the first Batgirl. A teen-ager, she was Batwoman's niece. You'll find her first adventure on page 255.

Then, in 1964, Batman did an about-face. His stories were a bit more realistic. The old stairway to the Batcave gave way to a new elevator. Batman now sported a yellow circle around his bat insignia. And the Bat-signal was largely replaced by the new hot line. Poor Alfred was killed off and replaced in the Wayne household by Dick's Aunt Harriet.

And then, in 1966, Batman became the first costumed crimebuster to have his own television show in *prime time!* Unfortunately for Batman fans, the series was deliberately campy. Many of the villains they used—such as The Bookworm, Ma Parker, Shame, Egghead—never appeared in the comics. Mr. Zero became Mr. Freeze; the Catwoman forgot—at least for a while—that she was supposed to have a crush on the Caped Crusader; the Joker was betrayed by his close-ups—his moustache showed under his makeup. Yet despite the absurdities, the TV series made the Dynamic Duo more famous than ever.

It spawned spin-offs, including two paperback novels (published by Signet) and a movie feature (one of the novels being taken from the script). When the live series was dropped, a cartoon series was done for the Saturday-morning kiddie crowd.

And the new Batgirl was born! She was Barbara Gordon, daughter of Commissioner Gordon. Now minus her glasses and bun, Babs holds forth in her own feature in *Detective Comics*. One other thing came from the TV show. Alfred was brought back to life—it turned out he had not died, but had been changed into a monstrous form and was the mysterious Outsider who had been plaguing Batman.

As the sixties ended, a new change came about. Robin went to college! Bruce Wayne then moved to a penthouse in Gotham City and founded the Victims, Incorporated, Program (V.I.P.)—all of which you can see beginning on page 299. This was followed soon after by the reappearance of the dark, avenging figure of mystery called *The* Batman!! (*See* page 337.) Robin continued with his own feature—first in *Detective*, then in *Batman*. (He had done some soloing back around 1950, in *Star-Spangled Comics*.) Man-Bat came on the scene, too (*see* page 353). By the way, he did *not* die; in "The Bride of Man-Bat," his sweetheart was changed into a creature like himself before Batman restored them both.

There's only one thing to add. The Batman newspaper strip was dropped many years ago; but with the advent of the TV series, a new Batman strip was created. It's still running in papers all over the world—and I'm proud to say that since last year, I have been writing the scripts for it! That kid that thrilled when The Batman came on the Superman show never dreamed that one day he'd be handling his hero's exploits. Wow!

**The first
BATMAN COMIC
Spring, 1940**

CALM YOURSELF, MY BOY, AND TELL ME ALL ABOUT IT!

...WELL SIR... TONIGHT I CAME HOME EARLY, AND AS I WAS PASSING THE LIBRARY I HEARD A GROAN... I RUSHED IN AND THERE WAS MY FATHER LYING ON THE FLOOR, WITH A KNIFE IN HIM!

...AND AS I RUSHED IN, I GOT THE IMPRESSION OF SOMETHING LEAPING OUT OF THE WINDOW... I ALSO NOTICED THAT FATHER'S SAFE WAS OPENED...

...I PULLED THE KNIFE OUT OF MY FATHER'S BODY, AND TURNED HIM TOWARD ME JUST IN TIME TO HEAR HIM SAY...

...CONTRACT... CONTRACT... OHHHH!

...AND THEN HE DIED. THAT'S HOW I GOT MY FINGER PRINTS ON THE KNIFE... THAT'S THE TRUTH, COMMISSIONER!

HMM! DID YOUR DAD HAVE ANY ENEMIES OR PEOPLE WHO HAD AN INTEREST IN HIS BUSINESS ACTIVITIES?

...NOT THAT I KNOW OF, EXCEPT HIS THREE FORMER BUSINESS PARTNERS... LET'S SEE, THEY WERE STEVEN CRANE, PAUL ROGERS AND ALFRED STRYKER.

COMMISSIONER, THERE'S A MAN NAMED STEVE CRANE WHO WANTS TO SPEAK TO OLD LAMBERT... WHEN I TOLD HIM THAT OLD LAMBERT WAS MURDERED HE GOT VERY EXCITED AND WANTED TO SPEAK TO YOU!

THIS IS COMMISSIONER GORDON. WHAT'S THE TROUBLE?

YESTERDAY, MR. LAMBERT CALLED AND TOLD ME HE RECEIVED AN ANONYMOUS THREAT ON HIS LIFE... TODAY I RECEIVED THE SAME... THAT'S WHY I CALLED UP... AND I'M AFRAID I'LL BE NEXT... WHAT SHALL I DO?

WAIT... AND DO NOT LEAVE ANYBODY IN -- WE'LL BE OVER SOON AS WE CAN-- WHAT'S THAT, BRUCE?

HO HUM! I'LL LEAVE YOU HERE TO FINISH YOUR WORK... I'M GOING HOME.

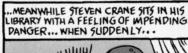

...MEANWHILE STEVEN CRANE SITS IN HIS LIBRARY WITH A FEELING OF IMPENDING DANGER... WHEN SUDDENLY...

AHHHHH!

...THERE IS A SICKENING SHOT... CRANE SLUMPS IN HIS CHAIR... DEAD! THE MURDERER RUSHES TO THE SAFE AND SECURES A PAPER...

DID YOU GET THE PAPER?

YEAH!

...AS THE TWO MEN LEER OVER THEIR CONQUEST, THEY DO NOT NOTICE A THIRD MENACING FIGURE STANDING BEHIND THEM... IT IS THE "BAT-MAN!"

THE BAT-MAN !!!...

THE "BAT-MAN" LASHES OUT WITH A TERRIFIC RIGHT...

...HE GRABS HIS SECOND ADVERSARY IN A DEADLY HEADLOCK...AND WITH A MIGHTY HEAVE...

SENDS THE BURLY CRIMINAL FLYING THROUGH SPACE...

THE "BAT-MAN" SWIFTLY PICKS UP THE PAPER THAT THE MURDERER STOLE FROM STEVEN CRANE'S SAFE...

...MEANWHILE THE COMMISSIONER DRAWS UP IN HIS CAR...

IT'S THE BAT-MAN! GET HIM!

MR. CRANE HAS BEEN MURDERED, SIR--IT'S HORRIBLE!

THAT'S TWO DEAD PARTNERS OUT OF THE FOUR THAT HAVE RECEIVED THREATENING NOTES, THE OTHER TWO MUST HAVE RECEIVED THEM TOO...LET'S GO TO ROGERS NEXT!

THE "BAT-MAN" READS THE PAPER HE SNATCHED FROM THE KILLERS AND A GRIM SMILE COMES TO HIS LIPS...

...HE SPEEDS HIS CAR FORWARD TO AN UNKNOWN DESTINATION...

...MEANWHILE ROGERS WHO HAS LEARNED OF LAMBERT'S DEATH BY NEWS BROADCAST, HAS ALREADY GONE TO THE NEIGHBORING LABORATORY OF HIS ERSTWHILE PARTNER, ALFRED STRYKER...

HELLO, JENNINGS. I MUST SEE STRYKER QUICKLY.

WON'T YOU COME IN?

SOCK!

JENNINGS, STRYKER'S ASSISTANT, CARRIES ROGERS TO THE BASEMENT OF HIS LABORATORY...

HEH! HEH! ONE MORE OUT OF THE WAY-- SOON I'LL CONTROL EVERYTHING!

THIS IS THE GAS-CHAMBER I USE TO KILL GUINEA PIGS, TO EXPERIMENT WITH-- BUT NOW YOU ARE MY GUINEA PIG ¿HEH-HEH!¿ WHEN THIS GLASS LID COVERS YOU ENTIRELY, GAS WILL COME THROUGH THE JET AND KILL YOU (HEH-HEH).

YOU FIEND!

JENNINGS PULLS A BRAKE WHICH STARTS THE GLASS DOWN OVER ROGERS AND CERTAIN DOOM...

I'M GOING DOWN NOW TO TURN THE GAS ON... SLEEP WELL... HEH-HEH!

...AT THAT MOMENT THE "BAT-MAN" LEAPS THROUGH AN OPEN TRANSOM...

...THE "BAT-MAN" SEIZES A WRENCH FROM A TABLE AND LEAPS FOR THE GAS-CHAMBER...

THE "BAT-MAN" QUICKLY PLUGS THE GAS-JET WITH A HANDKERCHIEF, AS THE GAS CHAMBER DESCENDS ENTIRELY OVER THEM...

SISSSS

...HE THEN UNTIES ROGERS, AND WITH A POWERFUL SWING...

CRASH

4

23

JENNINGS RETURNS AND IS STARTLED BY THE BAT-MAN ... HE REACHES FOR HIS GUN ...

WHAT TH--?

...THE "BAT-MAN" GREETS JENNINGS WITH A FLYING TACKLE...

MEANWHILE, ALFRED STRYKER HAS HEARD THE CRASH OF THE GAS-CHAMBER...AS HE ENTERS THE LABORATORY...

ROGERS? WHAT HAPPENED?

YOUR ASSISTANT, JENNINGS, TRIED TO KILL ME!

HOWEVER, STRYKER HAS NOT NOTICED THE "BAT-MAN" WHO HAS SECLUDED HIMSELF IN THE SHADOWS...

SO HE DIDN'T GET YOU AFTER ALL... WELL I'LL FINISH YOU AND THEN THROW YOUR BODY IN THE ACID TANK BELOW.

YOU!

OHHH! MY HAND~

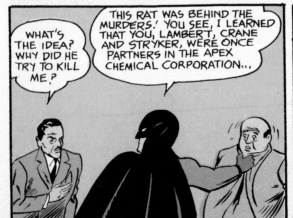

WHAT'S THE IDEA? WHY DID HE TRY TO KILL ME?

THIS RAT WAS BEHIND THE MURDERS! YOU SEE, I LEARNED THAT YOU, LAMBERT, CRANE AND STRYKER, WERE ONCE PARTNERS IN THE APEX CHEMICAL CORPORATION...,

...STRYKER, WHO WISHED TO BE SOLE OWNER, BUT HAVING NO READY CASH, MADE SECRET CONTRACTS WITH YOU, TO PAY A CERTAIN SUM OF MONEY EACH YEAR UNTIL HE OWNED THE BUSINESS. HE FIGURED BY KILLING YOU AND STEALING THE CONTRACTS, HE WOULDN'T HAVE TO PAY THIS MONEY.

HMM, A VERY CLEVER SCHEME, AND BEING THE CONTRACTS WERE A STRICT SECRET BETWEEN THE FOUR OF US, OUR HEIRS OR THE OUTSIDE WORLD WOULDN'T KNOW A THING ABOUT THEM... BUT HOW DID YOU KNOW ALL THIS?

I SECURED THIS CONTRACT FROM ONE OF HIS HIRED KILLERS.

...SUDDENLY, STRYKER, WITH THE STRENGTH OF A MADMAN, TEARS HIMSELF FREE FROM THE GRASP OF THE BAT-MAN...

SOCK!

HE'S FALLING RIGHT INTO THE ACID TANK!

YA-AA-AAAA-

A FITTING ENDING FOR HIS KIND.

..HOW CAN I EVER THANK YOU.., WHY-- GONE.'

THE NEXT DAY, YOUNG BRUCE WAYNE IS AGAIN A VISITOR AT THE COMMISSIONER'S HOUSE... WHO HAS JUST FINISHED TELLING BRUCE THE LATEST EXPLOITS OF THE "BAT-MAN".'

...AND THEN ROGERS SAID THE BAT-MAN WENT THROUGH THE SKYLIGHT.'

HMM! A VERY LOVELY FAIRY-TALE, COMMISSIONER, INDEED.

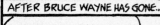

AFTER BRUCE WAYNE HAS GONE.. ...BRUCE WAYNE IS A NICE YOUNG CHAP--BUT HE CERTAINLY MUST LEAD A BORING LIFE... SEEMS DISINTERESTED IN EVERYTHING.

BRUCE WAYNE RETURNS HOME TO HIS ROOM... A LITTLE LATER HIS DOOR SLOWLY OPENS...

...AND REVEALS ITS OCCUPANT... IF THE COMMISSIONER COULD SEE HIS YOUNG FRIEND NOW... HE'D BE AMAZED TO LEARN THAT HE IS THE "BAT-MAN!"

Rob't Kane

FINIS

WATCH FOR A NEW THRILLING "BAT-MAN" STORY

NEXT MONTH!

26

THE BOY'S EYES ARE WIDE WITH TERROR AND SHOCK AS THE HORRIBLE SCENE IS SPREAD BEFORE HIM.

FATHER.. MOTHER !

.. DEAD! THEY'RE D..DEAD

DAYS LATER, A CURIOUS AND STRANGE SCENE TAKES PLACE

AND I SWEAR BY THE SPIRITS OF MY PARENTS TO AVENGE THEIR DEATHS BY SPENDING THE REST OF MY LIFE WARRING ON ALL CRIMINALS.

AS THE YEARS PASS BRUCE WAYNE PREPARES HIMSELF FOR HIS CAREER. HE BECOMES A MASTER SCIENTIST.

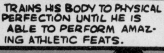

TRAINS HIS BODY TO PHYSICAL PERFECTION UNTIL HE IS ABLE TO PERFORM AMAZING ATHLETIC FEATS.

DAD'S ESTATE LEFT ME WEALTHY. I AM READY.. BUT FIRST I MUST HAVE A DISGUISE.

CRIMINALS ARE A SUPERSTITIOUS COWARDLY LOT. SO MY DISGUISE MUST BE ABLE TO STRIKE TERROR INTO THEIR HEARTS. I MUST BE A CREATURE OF THE NIGHT, BLACK, TERRIBLE.. A A..

- AS IF IN ANSWER, A HUGE BAT FLIES IN THE OPEN WINDOW!

A BAT! THAT'S IT! IT'S AN OMEN.. I SHALL BECOME A BAT!

AND THUS IS BORN THIS WEIRD FIGURE OF THE DARK.. THIS AVENGER OF EVIL. "THE BATMAN"

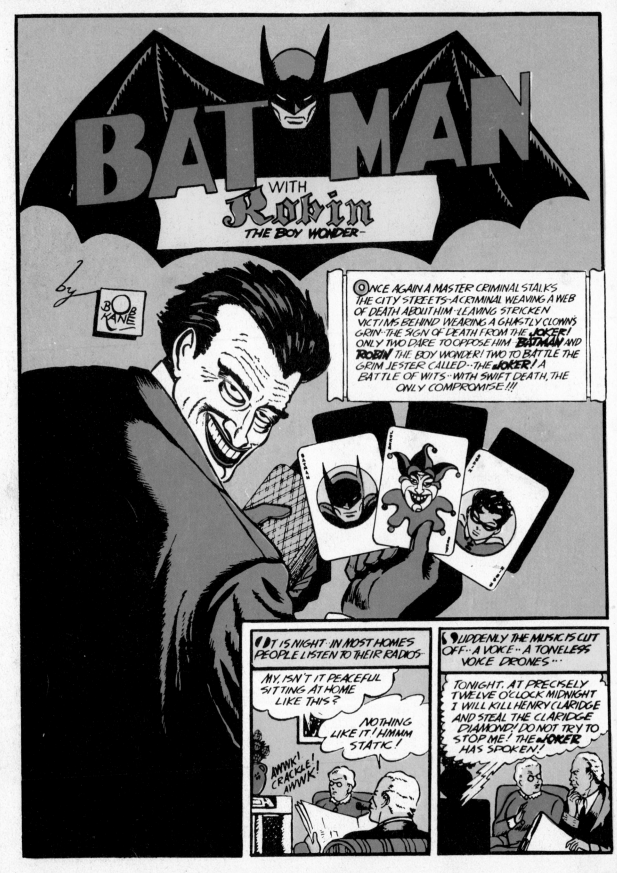

THEN ONCE AGAIN MUSIC....

HENRY. DID YOU HEAR? HENRY CLARIDGE. THE MILLIONAIRE, TO BE KILLED. THE FAMOUS DIAMOND STOLEN!

HAW! THAT'S JUST A GAG LIKE THAT FELLOW WHO SCARED EVERYBODY WITH THAT STORY ABOUT MARS THE LAST TIME! HA! HA! PAY NO ATTENTION TO IT, DEAR!

RADIO STATIONS ARE SWAMPED WITH CALLS! OFFICIALS DECLARE THE STRANGE MESSAGE IS NOT A PART OF THE PROGRAM...THE "GAG" HAS BECOME A REALITY!

HENRY CLARIDGE, FRANTIC WITH FEAR, CALLS THE POLICE

YOU'VE GOT TO PROTECT ME! I'M GOING TO BE KILLED ROBBED!

DON'T WORRY, MR. CLARIDGE. YOU, AND THAT DIAMOND OF YOURS WILL BE SAFE ENOUGH! WE'LL ALL STAY IN THE SAME ROOM WHERE THE DIAMOND IS KEPT, AND WATCH YOU

BONG! BONG!

ELEVEN O'CLOCK! ONE HOUR TO GO!

AN INFLEXIBLE CORDON IS FORMED ABOUT THE DOOMED MAN!

TIME DRAGS ON SECONDS MINUTES THEN THE FATAL HOUR TWELVE O'CLOCK!

I'M STILL ALIVE! I'M NOT DEAD! I'M SAFE!...

THE JOKER HAS FULFILLED HIS THREAT CLARIDGE IS DEAD!!

SLOWLY THE FACIAL MUSCLES PULL THE DEAD MAN'S MOUTH INTO A REPELLANT, GHASTLY GRIN, THE SIGN OF DEATH FROM THE JOKER!

IT'S..IT'S HORRIBLE!

GROTESQUE! THE JOKER BRINGS DEATH TO HIS VICTIMS WITH A SMILE!

THEN...WITHOUT WARNING!

..I'M SAAA-- AAGH! AAG-H-H!

DEAD..IT ISN'T POSSIBLE AND YET..

CHIEF! LOOK.. HIS MOUTH!

WHAT NOW, CHIEF?

THE CLARIDGE DIAMOND!—IF THE JOKER KILLED CLARIDGE, HE MUST HAVE THE DIAMOND!

BUT HOW COULD HE? WE WERE IN THE ROOM ALL THE TIME!

THE DIAMOND! THE JOKER DIDN'T GET IT AFTER ALL!

HE DID GET IT! THIS IS A PHONEY! IT'S GLASS!

CHIEF! I FOUND SOMETHING IN HERE! IT WAS UNDERNEATH THE CASE!

THE SIGN OF THE JOKER!

NOT FAR AWAY SITS A MAN... A MAN WITH A CHANGELESS, MASK-LIKE FACE... BUT FOR THE EYES... BURNING, HATE-FILLED EYES!

THE CLARIDGE DIAMOND—MINE! THOSE BUNGLING POLICE... HOW THEY WOULD LIKE TO KNOW HOW I MANAGED IT! AND HOW I SHOULD LIKE TO SHOUT THE ANSWER INTO THEIR STUPID FACES!

A SOLUTION INJECTED INTO SLEEPING CLARIDGE AT TWELVE LAST NIGHT... A SOLUTION THAT KILLS IN EXACTLY TWENTY-FOUR HOURS... SO THAT HE DIED AT TWELVE TONIGHT!

THEY FIND THE GLASS DIAMOND TO-NIGHT, THAT I EXCHANGED FOR THE REAL ONE LAST NIGHT! A PREDICTION ON THE RADIO OF A CRIME THAT HAS ALREADY BEEN DONE!

MAN SMILES... A SMILE WITHOUT MIRTH... RATHER A SMILE OF DEATH! THE AWESOME, GHASTLY GRIN OF... THE JOKER!

IF THE POLICE EXPECT TO PLAY AGAINST THE JOKER, THEY HAD BEST BE PREPARED TO BE DEALT FROM THE BOTTOM OF THE DECK.

NEWSPAPERS... RADIOS ALL SCREAM THE STORY OF THE RUTHLESS, CUNNING CRIMINAL THE JOKER! AT HOME BRUCE WAYNE, THE BATMAN, SPEAKS WITH HIS YOUNG AID, DICK GRAYSON, KNOWN AS ROBIN, THE BOY WONDER!

BUT BRUCE, WHY DON'T WE TAKE A SHOT AT THIS JOKER GUY?

NOT YET, DICK. THE TIME ISN'T RIPE, BUT WHEN WE DO ...

ANOTHER NIGHT·ANOTHER BREAK·AGAIN THE SAME DEADLY·MOCKING·VOICE··

AWWK··TONIGHT·IN EXACTLY ONE HOUR I WILL KILL JAY WILDE AND STEAL THE RONKERS RUBY! THE JOKER HAS SPOKEN!

IT'S NINE NOW! AT TEN O'CLOCK THAT FIEND WILL KILL JAY WILDE!

IT'S HIM AGAIN··THE JOKER!

AGAIN A WALL OF HUMANS ENCIRCLES A DOOMED MAN!!

I'M GOING TO DIE! IN FIVE MINUTES I'M GOING TO DIE! DIE! DIE!

THE TOLL OF TIME·THE FATAL HOUR!

BONG BONG BONG

TEN! IT'S GOING TO HAPPEN NOW! THE CLOCK IS TICKING MY LIFE AWAY!

A STRANGLED SCREAM··DEATH!

AAAGH

···FOLLOWED BY A STRANGE GAS···

FROM THE ARMOR THE JOKER!!!

LUCKY FOR THE POLICE THAT THE VENOM SPRAY ONLY PARALYSES FOR THE WHILE ELSE THEY WOULD HAVE PERISHED LIKE WILDE! HE HAD NO SPRAY BUT A BLOWN DART!

YOU HAD THE CONCENTRATED VENOM ON THE DART, EH WILDE? DIDN'T YOU EH? ARE YOU SO HAPPY THAT YOU SMILE FOR JOY. EH? I'M GLAD I HAVE BROUGHT YOU SO MUCH CHEER··

THE DIABOLICAL JOKER REMOVES THE ARMOR· STEALS THE RONKERS RUBY·

THANK YOU, ALL GENTLEMEN. YOU HAVE ME HAPPY TOO! WE SHALL MEET AGAIN!

4

THE POLICE SEARCH EVERYWHERE FOR THE **JOKER** BUT TO NO AVAIL. BUT ANOTHER GROUP IS ALSO INTERESTED THE CRIMINAL! ...A HANGOUT NOTED FOR ITS CRIMINAL ELEMENT...

I TELL YA BOYS WE GOTTA GET THIS GUY, THE **JOKER**!

WE GET THE CLARIDGE DIAMOND LINED UP FOR AN EASY JOB AND *HE* PULLS THE JOB!

YOU'RE RIGHT, BRUTE, HE'S CUTTIN' IN ON OUR RACKET!

AND DON'T FORGET *WE* WERE GONNA TRY FOR THE RONKERS RUBY!

WHAT'RE WE GONNA DO, TAKE IT LYIN' DOWN?

I GOT AN IDEA! YOU GUYS GO OUT AND PASS THE WORD AROUND THAT BRUTE NELSON IS GONNA GET THE **JOKER** THAT HE THINKS THE **JOKER** IS A YELLER RAT!

THE SENSATIONAL NEWS THAT BRUTE NELSON IS GUNNING FOR THE **JOKER** TRAVELS THE CRIMINAL "GRAPE-VINE". THE **BATMAN** IS READY TO GO INTO ACTION!

I'M GOING TO THE HOME OF BRUTE NELSON! I HEARD SOME NEWS TODAY OVER THE "GRAPE-VINE" THAT MAKES ME THINK THE TIME IS RIPE!

WHERE ARE YOU GOING ALONE?

IT IS NIGHT...BRUTE NELSON SITS IN HIS PRIVATE HOUSE IN THE SUBERBS.

THE **JOKER**, EH. WHEN I GET THROUGH WITH HIM HE'LL BE A JOKE ALL RIGHT!

SUDDENLY A DRONING, DEADLY VOICE...A FUNEREAL FACE...WITH EYES RADIATING HATE

TALKING ABOUT ME?

THE JOKER!

SUDDENLY DOORS BURST OPEN...THE **JOKER** IS TRAPPED!!

VERY NEAT...THAT UGLY HEAD OF YOURS *DOES* HAVE A BRAIN!

SURE, I KNEW IF YOU GOT SORE ENOUGH YOU'D COME FOR ME!

SUDDENLY THE SCRAPE OF A FOOT IS HEARD UP ON THE STAIR THE MIGHTY **BATMAN**!

I'M AFRAID I WASN'T AS SILENT AS I HOPED TO BE!

THE **BATMAN**! HOW DID *HE* GET IN HERE?

THE **JOKER** IS MOMENTARILY FORGOTTEN AS THE **BATMAN** LEAPS DOWN THE STAIRS...

LOOK OUT!!... SHOOT HIM!

32

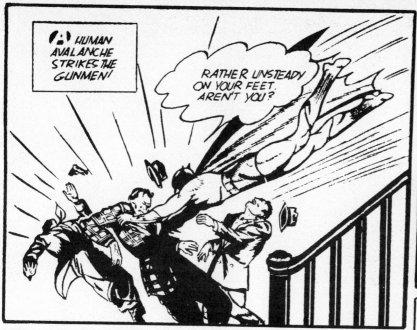

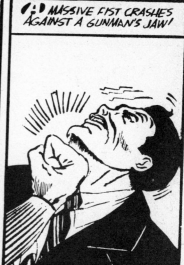

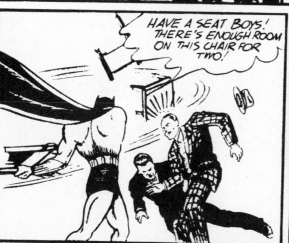

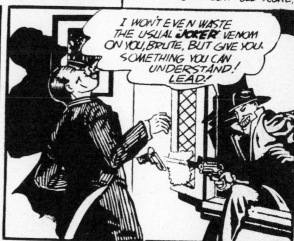

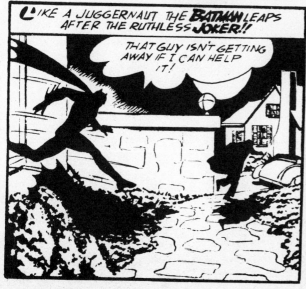

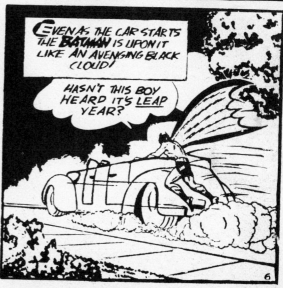

6

BUT THE JOKER HAS NOT RECKONED WITH THE AMAZING RECUPERATIVE POWERS OF THE MIGHTY BATMAN!

ROBIN··TIED··GOT TO GET OUT OF HERE!

AN ESCAPE FROM A FIERY DEATH!

FEW MOMENTS LATER·

THE JOKER IS GONE! I'D GIVE ANYTHING TO KNOW WHERE!

HE BOASTED INSIDE THAT HE WAS GOING TO GET THE CLEOPATRA NECKLACE NEXT!

THE CLEOPATRA NECKLACE!··THAT'S OWNED BY OTTO DREXEL! C'MON. THERE'S NOT A MOMENT TO LOSE··WITH A MANIAC ON THE LOOSE!

OTTO DREXEL LIVES ON THE PENTHOUSE IN THAT BUILDING ACROSS THE STREET!

IF WE CAN ONLY GET UP THERE BEFORE THE JOKER DOES!

ON THE PENTHOUSE. THE JOKER PREPARES TO ENTER.

BUT LEAPING FROM THE SCAFFOLD·· THE COWLED BATMAN··

STILL AT IT· EH?

THE SMASHING KICK SENDS THE *JOKER* FLYING OFF THE SCAFFOLDING!

AS THE FRANTIC MAN FALLS PAST THE PENTHOUSE BALLUSTRADE, A HAND REACHES OUT...

AAGH! I'M FALLING!

OH NO YOU'RE NOT!

THE STRONG ARM OF THE BATMAN HAULS HIM BACK TO SAFETY!

YOU'RE TOO VALUABLE A PRIZE TO LOSE!

YOU PLAYED YOUR LAST HAND, JOKER!

A FINAL BLOW WITH ALL THE STRENGTH OF THE *BATMAN* BEHIND IT!!

NEXT DAY...

DAILY STAR 2¢

BATMAN CAPTURES JOKER

LEAVES JOKER IN FRONT OF POLICE STATION DRIVE...

BUT WHAT I'D LIKE TO KNOW IS HOW HIS VICTIM'S MOUTHS TURNED UP IN THAT TERRIBLE GRIN!!

SOME SORT OF DRUG THAT PULLED THE MUSCLES OF THE FACE! THE *JOKER* WAS A CLEVER BUT DIABOLICAL KILLER! TOO CLEVER AND TOO DEADLY TO BE FREE!

BUT EVEN AS BRUCE SPEAKS, AT THE STATE PRISON, THE JOKER IS PLANNING, PLOTTING FOR HIS ESCAPE!

THEY CAN'T KEEP ME HERE! I KNOW OF A WAY OUT - THE *JOKER* WILL YET HAVE THE LAST LAUGH!

BOB KANE

THE Amazing BATMAN

AMERICA'S MOST FAMOUS ADVENTURE-STRIP CHARACTER... WITH THAT SENSATIONAL NEW DISCOVERY, THAT LAUGHING YOUNG DARE DEVIL Robin THE BOY WONDER WILL THRILL YOU EVERY MONTH WITH THEIR ASTOUNDING EXPLOITS IN DETECTIVE COMICS

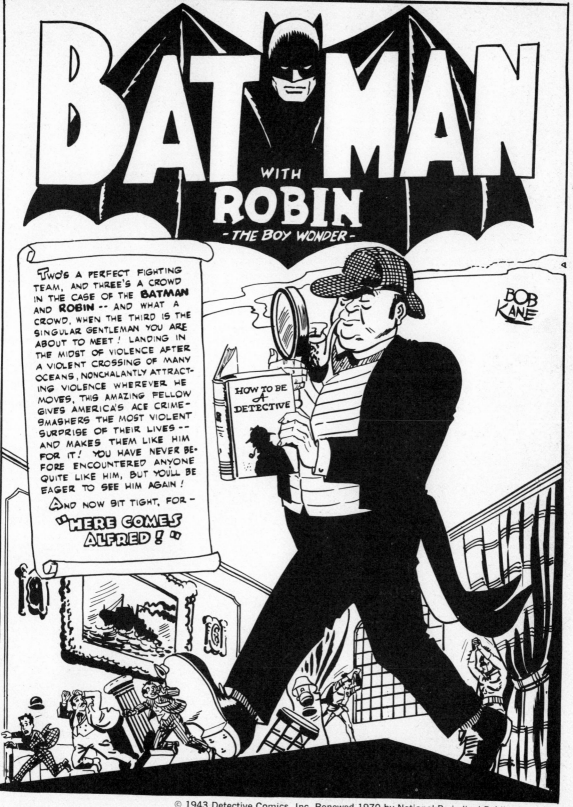

BAT MAN

WITH
ROBIN
- THE BOY WONDER -

TWO'S A PERFECT FIGHTING TEAM, AND THREE'S A CROWD IN THE CASE OF THE **BATMAN** AND **ROBIN** -- AND WHAT A CROWD, WHEN THE THIRD IS THE SINGULAR GENTLEMAN YOU ARE ABOUT TO MEET ! LANDING IN THE MIDST OF VIOLENCE AFTER A VIOLENT CROSSING OF MANY OCEANS, NONCHALANTLY ATTRACTING VIOLENCE WHEREVER HE MOVES, THIS AMAZING FELLOW GIVES AMERICA'S ACE CRIME-SMASHERS THE MOST VIOLENT SURPRISE OF THEIR LIVES -- AND MAKES THEM LIKE HIM FOR IT ! YOU HAVE NEVER BEFORE ENCOUNTERED ANYONE QUITE LIKE HIM, BUT YOU'LL BE EAGER TO SEE HIM AGAIN !

AND NOW SIT TIGHT, FOR -
"HERE COMES ALFRED!"

BOB KANE

HOW TO BE A DETECTIVE

NIGHT--AND A SMALL PASSENGER VESSEL ENDS A PERILOUS WAR-TIME CROSSING OF THE ATLANTIC AT A GOTHAM CITY PIER...

TWO SHIPBOARD ACQUAINT-ANCES SAY GOODBYE, NEVER DREAMING THAT THE HAND OF FATE WILL CAST THEM TOGETHER AGAIN SOONER THAN THEY THINK...

THE PARTIN' OF THE 'WAYS, MR. LEDUC! IT'S BEEN A PLEASURE TALKIN' TO YOU--AND I WISH YOU THE BEST, AND ALL THAT BALLY TOSH!

AH, MY ENGLISH FRIEND, I HOPE YOU FIND HAPPINESS AND SUCCESS IN THIS STRANGE LAND OF AMERICA!

YOU'RE GASTON LEDUC, EH? AND THIS IS YOUR PERMIT TO ENTER THE COUNTRY WITHOUT UNDERGOING INSPECTION... ALL RIGHT--YOU MAY PASS!

CUSTOMS INSPECTION

"HOW TO BE A DETECTIVE IN TEN EASY LESSONS"... SO YOU'RE A SLEUTH?

AND RAWTHER GOOD AT IT, IF I DO SAY SO!

HMMM... I'VE KNOWN ALL ALONG THERE WAS SOMETHIN' MYSTER-IOUS ABOUT THAT GENTLEMAN!

TRY AS I WOULD I COULDN'T MAKE HIM TALK ABOUT HIM-SELF! I'VE HALF A MIND TO FOLLOW HIM NOW!

WELL, IT'S A FREE COUNTRY, AND YOU'RE IN IT! ...NEXT!

AT THE PIER EXIT, THREE SWARTHY INDIVIDUALS WATCH THE NEW ARRIVALS WITH BEADY, GLITTERING EYES...

ON GUARD! IF YOU MISS OUR MAN, MY DAGGER WILL NOT MISS YOUR SCRAWNY BODIES!

I AM NOT AFRAID, MANUEL! MY EYES ARE AS KEEN AS YOUR KNIVES!

AND IN TURN, THE WATCHERS ARE WATCHED BY TWO DARK FIGURES THAT BLEND OMIN-OUSLY WITH THE SHADOWS!

SO THAT'S MANUEL STILETTI, THE INTER-NATIONAL CROOK! WHAT DO YOU THINK HE'S UP TO, BATMAN?

THAT'S WHAT I WANT TO FIND OUT! ALL I KNOW IS, WHEN-EVER MANUEL AND HIS CUTTHROATS ARE ON THE PROWL, TROUBLE ISN'T FAR AWAY!

PRESENTLY...

TWO YEARS LATE ALREADY, SO IT WON'T MATTER IF I TAKE AN HOUR OR TWO MORE TO FOLLOW LEDUC AND SATISFY MY CURIOSITY!

I'M

STEAMS

PIER 2

IT IS HE! REGARD THE VALISE!

HE SHALL NOT ESCAPE US!

GIVE ME THE VALISE QUIETLY, AMIGO, AND PERHAPS I SHALL LET YOU LIVE!

OTHERWISE, YOU ARE DEAD LIKE A DOG!

EH--WHAT?...OH-H-A BALLY STICKUP, SUCH AS I'VE SEEN IN THE CINEMA!...

LATER, AS THE ADVENTURERS PREPARE TO GO TO BED...

THAT WAS A GOOD ONE, **BRUCE**--TELLING HIM TO CALL ON US, WHEN NOBODY KNOWS WHO THE **BATMAN** AND **ROBIN** ARE, OR WHERE THEY LIVE!

OH WELL--MAYBE HE FANCIES HE'S SMART ENOUGH TO FIND US!

IMAGINE A DIMWIT LIKE HIM FINDING US WHEN SOME OF THE SMARTEST MEN IN THE WORLD HAVE TRIED AND FAILED!... OH, OH-- SOMEONE'S AT THE DOOR!

I'LL ANSWER IT!

R-I-N-G-G-G!!

WHO CAN IT BE AT THIS HOUR?

PROBABLY SOME OF YOUR NIGHT-OWL SOCIETY FRIENDS!

THE NEXT INSTANT....

GOOD EVENIN', GENTLEMEN! I TRUST I HAVEN'T DISTURBED YOUR REST!

HUH?

I'LL JUST SET MY LUGGAGE DOWN, IF YOU'LL PERMIT ME-- AND THEN WE'LL DISCUSS MY DUTIES!

WHAT A TIME I HAD GETTIN' HERE, MR. **WAYNE**! IT WAS NECESSARY TO WAIT A YEAR FOR A SHIP IN ENGLAND--AND THE ONE I FINALLY GOT, STARTED BY WAY OF THE INDIAN OCEAN!

BUT-- BUT -- BUT --

TWO SHIPS WERE TORPEDOED UNDER ME AND I SPENT A FORTNIGHT ADRIFT ON A LIFE RAFT! BUT MY MOST MEMORABLE EXPERIENCE HAPPENED WITHIN THE HOUR, WHEN THUGS ATTACKED ME AND THE **BATMAN** AND **ROBIN** DROVE THEM OFF!

WHY, THEN-- YOU DIDN'T KNOW--

QUIET, **DICK**!

I'VE ALWAYS ADMIRED THE **BATMAN** AS A BROTHER CRIMINOLOGIST, Y'KNOW-- BUT WOULD YOU BELIEVE IT, WHEN HE AWSKED ME TO CALL, I QUITE FORGOT TO AWSK HIS ADDRESS!

WELL!

④

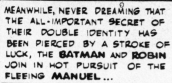

MEANWHILE, NEVER DREAMING THAT THE ALL-IMPORTANT **SECRET** OF THEIR DOUBLE IDENTITY HAS BEEN PIERCED BY A STROKE OF LUCK, THE **BATMAN** AND **ROBIN** JOIN IN HOT PURSUIT OF THE FLEEING **MANUEL**...

THERE THEY ARE-- TURNING THAT CORNER AHEAD!

STEP ON IT! IF WE DON'T CATCH THEM NOW, WE MAY NEVER HAVE ANOTHER CHANCE!

MOMENTS LATER...

THERE'S THEIR CAR-- BUT WHERE ARE THEY?

I CAN'T THINK OF ANY BETTER HIDEOUT THAN AN ABANDONED THEATER!

STEEL MUSCLES FORCE A LOCKED DOOR, AND THE DYNAMIC DUO VENTURES INTO COBWEB-DRAPED DARKNESS...

SPOOKY PLACE, ISN'T IT? I'LL BET NOBODY'S BEEN HERE FOR YEARS!

YOU'D LOSE YOUR MONEY! EVEN **ALFRED** WOULD KNOW BETTER SEEING THESE FOOT-PRINTS IN THE DUST!

BRRR-R-R! I CAN HEAR THE GHOSTS OF DEAD PLAYS MOANING!

THERE'S A STRANGE WHIRRING SOUND COMING FROM SOMEWHERE!

NOW, TOMAS!

LOOK OUT!-- ROBIN!

A STRANGE SOUND IN-DEED -- AND AN OMINOUS ONE -- FOR IT IS MADE BY WHIRRING ENDS OF WEIGHTED ROPES SWUNG BY AN EXPERT HAND IN THE SHADOWS OF A BOX...

TOO LATE! THE NEXT INSTANT, HISSING COILS WHIP AROUND THE LIMBS AND BODIES OF THE STARTLED CRIME-CRUSHERS...

WHA--? A BOLA!

I CAN'T MOVE MY ARMS OR FEET! I'M FALLING!

AS FINE A CAST AS WAS EVER MADE! **NOW** TO FINISH THEM!

NOT YET! LET US DO ALL OUR KILLING AT ONCE, AND DIS-POSE OF THE BODIES TOGETHER! THESE STUPID ONES WILL BE SAFE IF WE TIE THEM TIGHTER AND HOIST THEM INTO THE AIR!

BOUND AND GAGGED, THE HAPLESS PRISONERS ARE HOISTED ALOFT...

AT LAST YOU HAVE BEEN OUTWITTED, BATMAN! YOU CANNOT SHOUT FOR HELP -- AND IF YOU BREAK YOUR BONDS, YOU WILL BE DASHED TO PIECES BY THE FALL!

SOON WE SHALL BURN THE THEATER ABOUT YOUR EARS -- BUT FIRST, WE SHALL BRING A THIRD VICTIM TO SHARE YOUR FIERY FATE!

WE HAVE LEARNED THE THIRD MAN'S IDENTITY AND PRESENT ADDRESS FROM THE LABELS ON THE VALISE WHICH GAVE US SO MUCH TROUBLE! THEY FORMED A CODE MESSAGE SENT BY OUR CLEVER COLLEAGUES ABROAD!

DEATH FOR YOU AND A VAST FORTUNE FOR US! IS IT NOT DROLL?

LEFT ALONE, THE PLIGHT OF THE BATMAN AND ROBIN SEEMS HOPELESS...

WE'VE BEEN IN TIGHT SPOTS BEFORE, BUT I CAN'T SEEM TO RECALL ANY TIGHTER THAN THIS!

IF ONLY THEY HADN'T GAGGED US! IT MIGHT HELP TO TALK THINGS OVER!

OR PERHAPS THE BATMAN HAS BEEN HERE AND GONE... NO SIGN OF HIM ...HMMM -- QUITE A WHILE SINCE I'VE STOOD BEHIND THE FOOTLIGHTS!

OUTSIDE THE ANCIENT THEATER, THE TWO CRIMINALS ARE JOINED BY THEIR COMPANION...

WE THOUGHT THE POLICE WOULD HAVE YOU BY NOW, AND WE WERE HEART-BROKEN BECAUSE YOU WOULD MISS YOUR SHARE OF THE SWAG!

YOU MEAN, YOU'RE HEARTBROKEN BECAUSE I'M HERE TO CLAIM IT!... IT WAS A SIMPLE MATTER TO ESCAPE FROM THAT PIGHEADED BUTLER!

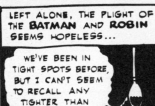

"ONCE A MUSIC HALL ACTOR, ALWAYS A HAM," IS A SAYING THAT HOLDS GOOD HERE AS ELSEWHERE...

PUTS ME IN MIND OF THE TIME I PLAYED THE ROLE OF A COCKNEY BUTLER IN A HAUNTED HOUSE... HOW DID IT GO... 'ARK -- WOT'S THAT NOISE? CAN IT BE H'ANOTHER SPIRIT COME TO 'AUNT ME?

WHILE BEHIND A CONVENIENT BARRIER...

PIGHEADED INDEED! I LET THE BLIGHTER ESCAPE SO I COULD FOLLOW HIM! THE BATMAN AND ROBIN MUST BE INSIDE AND I MAY AS WELL LET THEM SEE THAT I'M ON THE JOB!

HIGH OVERHEAD, AN UNAPPRECIATIVE AUDIENCE HEARS LINES OF LOWBROW MELODRAMA...

IF ONLY HE'D FORGET THE CORN AND LOOK THIS WAY!

THERE MUST BE SOME WAY TO ATTRACT HIS ATTENTION... MAYBE IF I START SWINGING..

H'I'M FAIR FED H'UP WITH GHOSTS, SO H'I H'AM! H'I SHALL TURN IN MY NOTICE!

BACK AND FORTH, IN EVER-WIDENING SWEEPS, THE **BATMAN** SWINGS HIS BODY-- UNTIL AT LAST HIS BOUND FEET CATCH ON A LOOSE ROPE...

HERE'S HOPING IT WORKS!

WONDER WHAT HE'S UP TO?

WRITHING LIKE A SERPENT, THE ROPE WHIPS ACROSS THE STAGE...

H'AWAY, H'AWAY, YE BLOOMIN' SPECTER! KEEP YER GHOSTLY FINGERS H'OFF ME!

OH-H-H-H! IT'S REALLY HAPPENIN'!

S-W-I-S-I

WELL! FOR A MOMENT I THOUGHT-- EH? ... WHY, THERE ARE THE **BATMAN** AND **ROBIN** IN DISTRESS!

AND AT THIS VERY MOMENT, MANUEL AND HIS THUGS ARE ENTERING AN APARTMENT IN AN EXCLUSIVE NEIGHBORHOOD...

AND THAT MIGHT BRING THE POLICE!

SOFTLY! IF WE AWAKEN THE OTHERS, WE SHALL HAVE TO USE OUR GUNS!

AND ALFRED'S MYSTEROUS FRIEND OF THE SHIP HAS A RUDE AWAKENING...

NOT A SOUND, DUKE, OR YOU ARE A DEAD MAN!

NO, YOU MUST NOT TAKE THE CROWN JEWELS! I BROUGHT THEM HERE TO ESTABLISH CREDITS FOR MY GOVERNMENT-IN-EXILE!

BAH-- WHAT DO WE CARE FOR YOUR GOVERNMENT? SILENCE HIM, PABLO!.

TO THINK HE BROUGHT THOSE JEWELS SECRETLY HALF AROUND THE WORLD, ONLY TO LOSE THEM AT THE END OF THE JOURNEY! IT SHOWS WHAT SHARP EYES AND EARS THE UNDERWORLD HAS!

AND IT SHOWS HOW PROMPTLY WE HAVE ACTED! ANOTHER TWO HOURS AND THE JEWELS WOULD HAVE BEEN IN A SAFE-DEPOSIT VAULT!

BACK IN THE THEATER...

AH, **BATMAN**-- I SEE YOU HAVE WAITED!

AS A REWARD, YOU SHALL HAVE DISTINGUISHED COMPANY WHEN THE FIRE STARTS -- A NOBLEMAN WHOSE FRIENDS WILL NEVER KNOW WHAT HAS HAPPENED TO HIM!

NOR WILL THE POLICE WHICH IS MORE IMPORTANT!

BUT WITH LIGHTNING SWIFTNESS, HOODED FIGURES PLUMMET FROM THE SHADOWS OVERHEAD!

YOU'RE ABOUT TO HAVE SOME DISTINGUISHED COMPANY YOUR-SELF -- AND WE'RE IT!

THIS CANNOT BE! IT IS A JOKE!

WHA--!

A JOKE ON YOU!

QUICKLY, TOMAS -- KILL THEM OR ALL IS LOST!

TIME TO RING DOWN THE CURTAIN ON THIS ACT!

LOOK OUT, TOMAS!

IT IS THE BATMAN WHO HAD BETTER LOOK OUT!

BEFORE DEADLY STEEL AND LEAD CAN STRIKE, ALFRED LOOSENS A ROPE IN THE WINGS... AND THE CURTAIN, WITH IT'S HEAVY WOODEN FRAMEWORK, HURTLES DOWNWARD!

THAT'S RIGHT-- TAKE A BOW! AH! GOOD WORK, OL' BEAN!

OOO-O-O...

A FITTING FINALE FOR A BAD ACTOR! EH, WOT?

HERE'S AN ALL-STAR ACT TO FINISH THE BILL!

SO THESE ARE WHAT THEY WERE AFTER! BUT WHERE DID THEY COME FROM AND WHO DO THEY REALLY BELONG TO?

IF YOU WILL PER-MIT ME, SIR, I CAN ELUCIDATE THE MYSTERY!

WH-WHERE AM I?

THEY ARE THE CROWN JEWELS OF THE COUNTRY OF WHICH THIS MAN-THE DUKE OF DORIAN -- IS THE PREMIER! HE BROUGHT THEM HERE SECRETLY FOR HIS GOVERN-MENT, BUT SOME-HOW THESE CRIMINALS GOT WIND OF IT!

MY FRIEND! YOU HAVE SAVED MY LIFE AND MY COUNTRY'S TREAS-URES -- AND TO THINK I LAUGHED WHEN YOU SAID YOU WERE AN AMATEUR DETECTIVE!

AND HE WASN'T THE ONLY ONE WHO LAUGHED!

The BAT-MAN

by Bob Kane

"THE BATMAN MEETS DOCTOR DEATH"

THE *BAT MAN*, EERY FIGURE OF THE NIGHT, HAS BECOME A LEGENDARY FIGURE IN THE LIFE OF THE TEEMING METROPOLIS, RIGHTING WRONGS AND BRINGING JUSTICE WHERE IT HAS NEVER BEEN BEFORE...

IN THE STUDY OF DOCTOR KARL HELLFERN, LATER TO BE MORE WIDELY KNOWN AS DOCTOR DEATH!

JABAH, COME HERE!

JABAH, I HAVE AT LAST COMPLETED ALL MY LABORATORY EXPERIMENTS. MY DEATH BY POLLEN EXTRACT IS DEFINITE. I AM READY TO EXACT MY TRIBUTE FROM THE WEALTHY OF THE WORLD. THEY WILL EITHER PAY TRIBUTE TO ME OR *DIE*, AND YET ONE THING TROUBLES ME ...

...THIS MAN THEY CALL THE BAT MAN A CRIME SUCH AS OURS IS SURE TO ATTRACT HIS ATTENTION. HE MUST BE DONE AWAY WITH! IF I KNEW WHO HE IS—BUT, NO ONE DOES. I MUST TRAP HIM!

— PERHAPS WE CAN CONTACT HIM THROUGH THE PERSONEL NOTICE COLUMN IN THE DAILY NEWSPAPERS...

ACROSS THE CITY, BRUCE WAYNE, IN REALITY THE *BAT MAN*, READS THE DAILY PAPER, THE NEXT MORNING...

HMM! WHAT'S THIS?

HAVE YOU A LETTER ADDRESSED TO JOHN JONES?

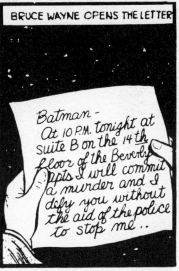
BRUCE WAYNE OPENS THE LETTER

BRUCE RETURNS HOME. HE KNEELS BEFORE A SMALL CHEST AND TAKES OUT HIS BAT-LIKE MANTLE...

HALF AN HOUR TO CHANGE AND HALF AN HOUR TO GET TO THE PENTHOUSE

THESE GLASS PELLETS OF CHOKING GAS MIGHT COME IN HANDY TONIGHT.. IF THIS IS WHAT I THINK IT IS.

LIKEWISE THESE SUCTION GLOVES AND KNEE PADS. THE PENT-HOUSE WILL REQUIRE A BIT OF CLIMBING.

IN PLACE OF BRUCE WAYNE, THE WEALTHY SOCIAL FIGURE - THE BATMAN!

THE BATMAN GLANCES AT THE DASHBOARD CLOCK -
8:30 EXACTLY. I'M OFF!

A FEW MINUTES BEFORE NINE, A CAR SLIDES TO A STOP NEAR THE DESIGNATED BUILDING.

55

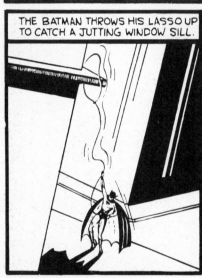

FOR A QUICK GETAWAY THE BATMAN HAS HIS ROPE HANDY.

THE BATMAN SURVEYS HIS GROUND CAUTIOUSLY...

UNSEEN BY THE BATMAN, ARE THE GUNMEN PLACED TO TRAP HIM BY DOCTOR DEATH.

HE BIT FOR IT! SHALL I GIVE IT TO HIM?

NO. THE DOCTOR SAID TO KILL HIM INSIDE SO'S THE POLICE WILL FIND HIM IN HERE. WAIT. HE'S COMING IN!

THE LIGHTS BLAZE ON - AND THE BATMAN IS CAUGHT IN A TRAP-

PUT 'EM UP BATMAN! WE'VE GOT YOU AT LAST!.

BUT THE GUNMEN RECKON WITHOUT THE GREAT SPEED AND AGILITY OF THE BATMAN

BANG

BANG!

—AND THE HIRED KILLERS GO DOWN...

QUICK AS A PANTHER THE BATMAN IS UPON THE GUNMEN LASHING OUT WITH BOTH FISTS...

...AND WHO SENT YOU, MAY I ASK?

WE CAN'T TELL YOU HE'D KILL US!

YOUR CHOICE GENTLEMEN! TELL ME! OR I'LL KILL YOU!

—GOOD EVENING, BATMAN. DOCTOR DEATH SENDS HIS GREETINGS...

JABAH FIRES!

THE BATMAN IS HIT!

THE WOUNDED BATMAN EJECTS A GLASS PELLET FROM HIS BELT.

THE BATMAN HOLDS HIS BREATH AND SLAMS THE GLASS PELLET ON THE FLOOR IN FRONT OF THE GIANT INDIAN...

UGH! I'M CHOKING!

THE ROOM BECOMES FILLED WITH A DEADLY GAS. THE WOUNDED BATMAN LEAPS FOR THE GLASS WINDOWS LEADING TO THE PENTHOUSE ROOF.

GAWD! HE'S JUMPED OFF

BUT WHAT THE GUNMEN OF DOCTOR DEATH FAIL TO SEE

THE BATMAN SWINGS ONTO A PROJECTING CORNICE OF THE ROOF

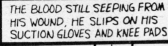

THE BLOOD STILL SEEPING FROM HIS WOUND, HE SLIPS ON HIS SUCTION GLOVES AND KNEE PADS.

THE BATMAN IN HIS CAR, PLACES A PAD OF COTTON ON HIS BARED SHOULDER.

THIS'LL KEEP UNTIL I GET TO A PHONE BOOTH.

DRESSED IN CIVILIAN CLOTHES ONCE MORE, BRUCE WAYNE, THE BATMAN, ENTERS A PHONE BOOTH..

DAILY GLOBE? I WANT THIS INSERTED IN YOUR PUBLIC NOTICE COLUMN: "I ACCEPT YOUR CHALLENGE, DOCTOR DEATH. THE BATMAN."

I GUESS I'D BETTER SEE THE FAMILY DOCTOR AT ONCE. THIS SHOULDER IS BEGINNING TO ACHE

IT'S ALL RIGHT NOW, BRUCE. BUT HOW DID YOU SHOOT YOURSELF WHEN THERE ARE NO POWDER MARKS ON YOUR FLESH?

I DO FUNNY THINGS SOMETIMES, DOC. I'LL TELL YOU ALL ABOUT IT SOMEDAY. THANKS FOR EVERYTHING.

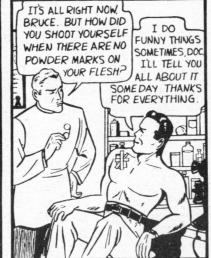

THE NEXT MORNING IN DOCTOR DEATH'S STUDY.

YOU FOOLS! YOU BUNGLERS! HE WALKS INTO A TRAP AND YOU LET HIM GO. IF YOU MISS THE NEXT TIME... FOLLOW ME, JABAH!

HERE IS A PICTURE OF JOHN P. VAN SMITH. HE REFUSES TO PAY TRIBUTE TO ME. HE MUST DIE! I HAVE IMMUNED YOU WITH MY SERUM FROM THIS POLLEN, WHICH YOU WILL BLOW AT YOUR VICTIM AS HE COMES FROM HIS CLUB TONIGHT

JABAH GOES ON HIS 'ERRAND OF DEATH'...

MY WOULD-BE KILLER OF LAST NIGHT! I THINK I'LL FOLLOW HIM.

AS THE UNSUSPECTING VICTIM STEPS FROM HIS CLUB...

HIS ERRAND FULFILLED, JABAH FLEES... BUT HE HAS NOT RECKONED UPON THE PRESENCE OF BRUCE WAYNE, THE BATMAN.

DON'T BREATHE OR YOU'RE DEAD!

I HAVEN'T TIME FOR QUESTIONS BUT I'VE A HUNCH THAT IF YOU HAD BREATHED IN WHAT THAT MAN BLEW, IT WOULD BE CURTAINS FOR YOU. I'VE GOT TO TRAIL HIM. ADIEU!

PREPARE FOR A VISIT TONIGHT, DOCTOR DEATH, FROM THE BATMAN.

THAT NIGHT, ON THE SIDEWALK BEHIND DOCTOR DEATH'S HOUSE

ON HIS ROPE, THE BATMAN CLIMBS TO THE SECOND STORY OF THE HOUSE.

ONLY A FEW MINUTES MORE DOCTOR DEATH. WE HAVE A SCORE TO EVEN.

A CREAK OF A GLASS CUTTER AND THE BATMAN ENTERS...

THE BATMAN FINDS DOCTOR DEATH AND HIS GIANT SERVANT JABAH IN THE LABORATORY.

IT WON'T BE LONG, DOCTOR.

A SNAP OF A LASSO AND JABAH IS JERKED FROM THE TABLE.

THE BATMAN!

GOOD EVENING DOCTOR—BUT IT WON'T BE... AFTER I'M THROUGH WITH YOU!

YOU FOOL

DOCTOR DEATH PRESSES A BUTTON AND DROPS INTO A SECRET CHUTE.

I CAN JUST MAKE IT BEFORE IT CLOSES—I HOPE!

HA-HA-HA-HEH-HEH!

INTO THE UNKNOWN, AFTER DOCTOR DEATH, PLUNGES THE BATMAN...

...WHO LANDS ON A MAT AND SEES DOCTOR DEATH DISAPPEARING DOWN THE HALL...

THE BATMAN PURSUES DOCTOR DEATH RELENTLESSLY.

DOCTOR DEATH RETURNS TO THE LABORATORY IN A LAST DESPERATE ATTEMPT TO ELUDE THE BATMAN.

THERE IS YET TIME.

THE BATMAN SEIZES A FIRE EXTINGUISHER ON THE WALL AND..

YOU ARE JUST TOO LATE, MY FOE. WATCH! THE FIERY DEATH__

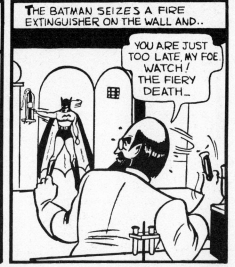

FLINGS IT AT DOCTOR DEATH KNOCKING THE DEADLY TUBE TO THE FLOOR WHERE IT SWIFTLY IGNITES INTO A BLAZING INFERNO!!!

HA! HA! OH__ HA-HA-HA.. YOU.. YOU FOOL!

YOU ARE THE POOR FOOL! HE HAS GONE MAD.

DEATH...TO DOCTOR DEATH!

...BUT IS IT DEATH TO THIS ARCH CRIMINAL? FOLLOW THE FURTHER AMAZING AND UNIQUE ADVENTURES OF THE

BAT-MAN

IN

Next Month's DETECTIVE COMICS

LATER HIS PART OF THE ACT OVER, THE BOY DICK IS GOING PAST MR. HALY'S ROOM WHEN HE HEARS VOICES...

AND IF YOU PAY US WE PROTECT YOU, GET IT HALY?

YES! I GET IT. YOU'RE GANGSTERS! IT'S A PROTECTION RACKET! I'LL CALL THE POLICE!

YOU DON'T WANT TO DIE, DO YOU? BE SENSIBLE PAY US AND PROTECT THE SHOW FROM "ACCIDENTS"

GET OUT! GET OUT!

OKAY BUDDY! IT'S YOUR FUNERAL REMEMBER... "ACCIDENTS" WILL HAPPEN!

THE NEXT NIGHT... IN THE AUDIENCE... BRUCE WAYNE, THE BATMAN, ENJOYS THE SHOW

...AND NOW THAT YOUNG DICK GRAYSON IS SAFE BELOW. THE FLYING GRAYSONS WILL PERFORM THEIR DEATH-DEFYING ACT... THE TRIPLE SPIN!

THE DRUMS ROLL GRAYSON FLYS OUT TURNS OVER THREE TIMES... AND STRAIGHTENS OUT

NICELY DONE, JOHN

SUDDENLY THE ROPES PART!!

JOHN!

MARY!

MOTHER! FATHER!

T-THEY'LL BE KILLED!

EEE-EE-EE

ARE ARE TH-THEY OH N-NO THEY...

I'M AFRAID SO, SON

LATER

YEAH! BUT THERE WOULDN'T BE ANY "ACCIDENTS" IF YOU PAID US TO PROTECT YOU!

TOO BAD ABOUT THAT "ACCIDENT," HALY

YOU MURDERERS. ALL RIGHT, I'LL PAY- BUT ONLY SO THAT NO ONE ELSE WILL BE KILLED

BUT OUTSIDE THE DOOR DICK LISTENS... WHEN...

THEY KILLED MY MOTHER AND FATHER! I'M GOING TO THE POLICE!

NO SON, NOT YET!

INSIDE THE MYSTERIOUS HOUSE···

WELL BOSS, THERE IT IS· THE TAKE OF THE WEEK!

IT ISN'T ENOUGH! SEE! YOU'VE GOT TO GET MORE MONEY OUT OF OUR CUSTOMERS. SEE! I WANT YOU TO GO TO THE BUTCHERS, THE TAILORS, LAUNDRYS AND THE REST AND MILK 'EM DRY, SEE!

ALL OF THEM GET IT, SEE! EVEN THE NEWSBOYS AND THE REST OF THE SMALL STUFF! AND IF THEY DON'T PLAY BALL, YOU KNOW WHAT TO DO, SEE!! START TOMORROW NIGHT!

TOMORROW NIGHT! WOW! I BETTER TELL THE BATMAN RIGHT AWAY!

NEXT NIGHT· A TAILOR STORE

BUT I CAN'T PAY YOU ANY MORE! I HAVEN'T GOT IT!

GET IT!

AND IF YOU DON'T

SUDDENLY FROM BEHIND···

DON'T TALK SO MUCH!!

HOLLOW··· JUST AS I THOUGHT!

IF YOU SEE BOSS ZUCCO, TELL HIM THE BATMAN WAS HERE· GOOD DAY GENTLEMEN!

IN A BUTCHER SHOP···

PAY UP OR ELSE YOU'LL··· WHA···?

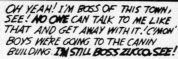

72

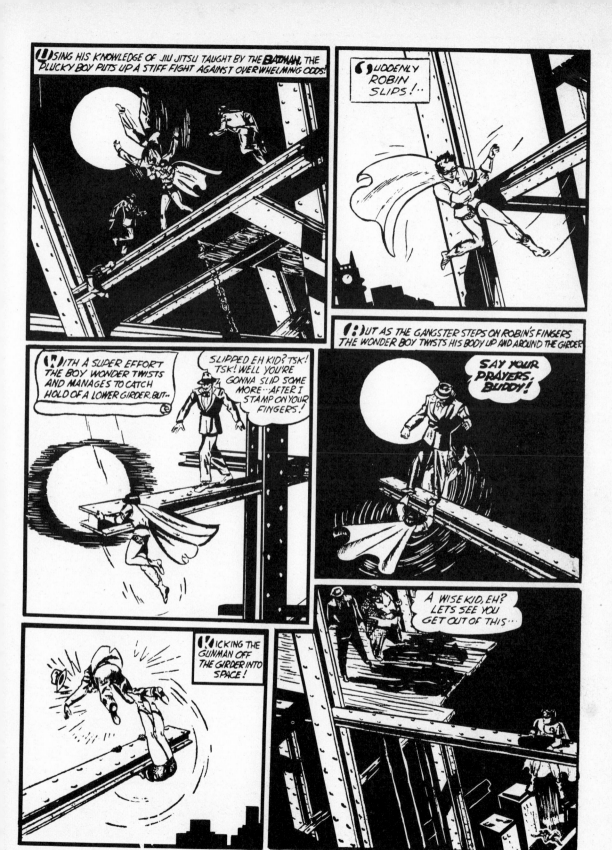

74

MR. KENNETH TODD IS THE NEW STAR OF THE PICTURE, "DREAD CASTLE." HE PLAYS "THE TERROR." YEARS AGO, IN THE OLD VERSION, THIS ROLE WAS PLAYED BY THE GREATEST CHARACTER AND MAKEUP ARTIST, BASIL KARLO!

DID SOMEONE SPEAK MY NAME? HELLO, BENTLEY.

BASIL KARLO!

JUST DROPPED IN TO WISH THE SUCCESSOR TO MY ROLE GOOD LUCK. TODD, I ONLY HOPE YOU ARE AS SMART AS I WAS FOOLISH. LOTS OF LUCK TO YOU!

THANK YOU, KARLO. I GUESS I'LL NEVER BE AS GOOD A CHARACTER ACTOR AS YOU WERE!

WHEN KARLO LEAVES...

OH, YOU REMEMBER HOW AFTER HE BECAME A BIG STAR HE GOT INTO SCRAPES AND DID A LOT OF CRAZY THINGS. HE GOT A LOT OF BAD PUBLICITY BECAUSE OF IT. AFTER THE PAPERS GOT THROUGH WITH HIM, THE PEOPLE WOULDN'T GO TO SEE HIS PICTURES EVEN IF THEY GAVE AWAY PRIZES!

WHAT DID KARLO MEAN BY THAT "SMART" AND "FOOLISH" CRACK?

AT THAT MOMENT

LOOK HERE, BENTLEY, WHAT'S THE IDEA OF STOPPING MY DIRECTING ON "DREAD CASTLE"?

NED NORTON.. SO YOU FINALLY SHOWED UP?

YOU GO OUT AND DISAPPEAR FOR DAYS AND YOU WANT TO KNOW WHY! FIRST PROVE YOU CAN BE RELIED ON AND THEN PERHAPS I'LL GIVE YOU WORK!

SO I'M FIRED, EH?

I WON'T FORGET THIS, BENTLEY. I WON'T FORGET THIS! REMEMBER, YOU'LL NEVER FINISH THIS PICTURE WITHOUT ME!

BENTLEY SHOWS BRUCE ABOUT THE STUDIO.

AND, THERE IN THE BACK IS THE SET OF "DREAD CASTLE." FOR THIS PICTURE I HAD A REAL CASTLE BUILT —WITH A MOAT AROUND IT! NO EXPENSE WAS SPARED!

SUDDENLY THE SOUND OF ANGRY VOICES REACHES THEM

WE'RE THROUGH, FRED WALKER, THROUGH! AND THAT'S FINAL!

OH, OH! A TIFF!

YOU CAN'T WALK OUT ON ME NOW! WHAT ABOUT OUR LOVE?

THAT'S LORNA DANE, MY STAR! SHE'S GETTING RID OF HER SWEETHEART, FRED WALKER, JUST LIKE SHE'S RID HERSELF OF ALL HER OTHER SWEETHEARTS, THE GOLD DIGGER!

AND NONE TOO GENTLY, EITHER!

OUR LOVE? HA! HA! DON'T MAKE ME LAUGH! LISTEN, FRED, YOU HAVEN'T HAD A ROLE IN MONTHS. I CAN'T AFFORD TO LET MYSELF BE TIED TO AN ACTOR THAT'S SLIPPING!

YOU VIXEN, I OUGHT TO KILL YOU! YOU DON'T DESERVE TO LIVE!

LAUGH AT ME, WILL YOU! WHEN I GET THROUGH WITH YOU, YOU WON'T LAUGH AGAIN ... EVER!

LATER... WELL, MR. BENTLEY. IT'S BEEN VERY ENJOYABLE, BUT IT'S GROWING LATE.

ALL RIGHT, TAKE JULIE HOME, BUT BE CAREFUL.... SHE IS VALUABLE PROPERTY—NOT ONLY TO ME BUT TO YOU, EH? HA! HA!

AS THEY LEAVE, A SATURNINE-LOOKING MAN APPROACHES BENTLEY....

HYA, BENTLEY. DECIDED TO ACCEPT MY OFFER YET?

ROXY BRENNER!

OFF! YOU GANGSTER! OFF THE LOT! I REFUSE TO PAY YOU "PROTECTION" MONEY! NOW GET OFF BEFORE I CALL THE POLICE!

OKAY, BENTLEY, IT'S YOUR FUNERAL! BUT DON'T BLAME ME IF ANYTHING HAPPENS TO ANY OF YOUR STARS!

NOBODY TALKS TO ROXY BRENNER LIKE THIS! WHEN I GET THROUGH WITH YOU, YOU'LL LEARN TO KEEP YOUR MOUTH SHUT! SEE YOU SOON, BENTLEY!

LATER...THE WAYNE HOME...

SOMETHING IS GOING TO HAPPEN OUT AT THE STUDIO! THERE SEEMS TO BE AN AURA OF HATE PERVADING THE VERY ATMOSPHERE OF THE PLACE! YESSIR! SOMETHING IS GOING TO HAPPEN—AND SOON!

3

THOUGH POLICE INVESTIGATE, AT THE END OF A WEEK THEY ARE FORCED TO REPORT..."LORNA DANE MURDERED BY PERSON OR PERSONS UNKNOWN!"

SOON A WORRIED JULIE VISITS BRUCE.

..AND NOW THE STUDIO IS GOING AHEAD WITH THE PICTURE..AND IN THE NEXT SCENE I'M SUPPOSED TO BE "KILLED" BY THE "TERROR". I'M AFRAID! SUPPOSE...

DON'T WORRY, DEAR! THE MURDERER WON'T TRY FOR YOU.. HE JUST WANTED TO KILL LORNA.

AS JULIE LEAVES..

I'M WORRIED MYSELF! SUPPOSE JULIE IS RIGHT! DICK! PUT ON YOUR OUTFIT! WE'RE GOING OUT!

A MOMENT LATER...
BATMAN, THE DARK KNIGHT, AND ROBIN, THE BOY WONDER

ALL SET?

LET'S GO!

THE GATES OF ARGUS PICTURES!

IT SAYS "NO ADMITTANCE"...BUT THAT DOESN'T MEAN US, ROBIN!

INSIDE THE STUDIO...

YOU SAID SOMETHING WOULD HAPPEN TO MY STARS..YOU.. YOU GANGSTER! DID YOU KILL LORNA DANE?

BETTER PAY UP, BENTLEY!

MAYBE..BETTER PAY UP THE "PROTECTION" MONEY OR ELSE YOU WON'T HAVE ANY DOUBTS!

SUDDENLY HURTLING THROUGH THE AIR... BATMAN AND ROBIN, THE BOY WONDER!!

I THINK YOU'RE THE ONE WHO IS LOOKING FOR TROUBLE!

WHA...? I'M ATTACKED BY AN ELF!

IF YOU'RE LOOKING FOR TROUBLE, BENTLEY, WHY...SAY...!!

MEANWHILE. WHAT OF **ROBIN**, WHO WALKS THE DESERTED STUDIO GROUNDS?

SUDDENLY HE SPIES... LIGHT ON DREAD CASTLE!

LIGHT! IT SEEMS I'M NOT THE ONLY ONE OUT TONIGHT!

...THINK I'LL INVESTIGATE!

BUT FROM HIGH ABOVE. THE BOY IS SPIED... THE MYSTERIOUS **CLAYFACE!**

HMM. SOMEONE IS INQUISITIVE... BUT NOT FOR LONG... AHAA!

ROBIN ENTERS THE GLOOMY CASTLE.

GOSH! WHAT A SPOT FOR A MURDER!

UNAWARE OF THE LURKING TERROR AT THE TOP. **ROBIN** ASCENDS THE LONG WINDING STAIRCASE TO THE LAST TOWER...

LOOKS LIKE MY GUEST IS WALKING HIS LAST MILE!

CLAYFACE LEAPS...

HEY!

BUT THE AGILE **ROBIN** DUCKS AND THE MURDEROUS **CLAYFACE** GOES HURTLING OVER HIS SHOULDER!

8

ONCE MORE IN THE TOWER·BUT CLAYFACE·GONE!

HE'S GONE! I WONDER WHAT HE WAS DOING UP HERE ANYWAY?

PROBABLY SURVEYING THE SCENE FOR HIS NEXT MURDER!··CLAYFACE ···I WONDER IF···

NEXT MORNING···IN A DIMLY-LIT ROOM, A MAN APPLIES A GROTESQUE MAKEUP·CLAYFACE!

ONCE MORE I DON THE GARMENTS OF DEATH!

THIS MORNING MISS JULIE BEGINS HER "MURDER" SCENE IN "DREAD CASTLE"··PERHAPS IT SHALL PROVE PROPHETIC! HA! PROPHETIC!

ON THE SET OF "DREAD CASTLE", THE CAMERAS GRIND WHILE JULIE IS UNAWARE OF IMPENDING DANGER.

AA-A-A-AAH! THE TERROR!

DIE!

BUT UP ON THE DARKENED CATWALK A GHASTLY FIGURE RAISES HIS KNIFE FOR THE THROW···CLAYFACE!

DIE-JULIE!

BUT SUDDENLY A ROPE ENCIRCLES THE MURDERER'S WRIST···

?

MAY I CUT IN?

···THEN WITH THE SPEED OF THOUGHT A MIGHTY TACKLE· BATMAN!

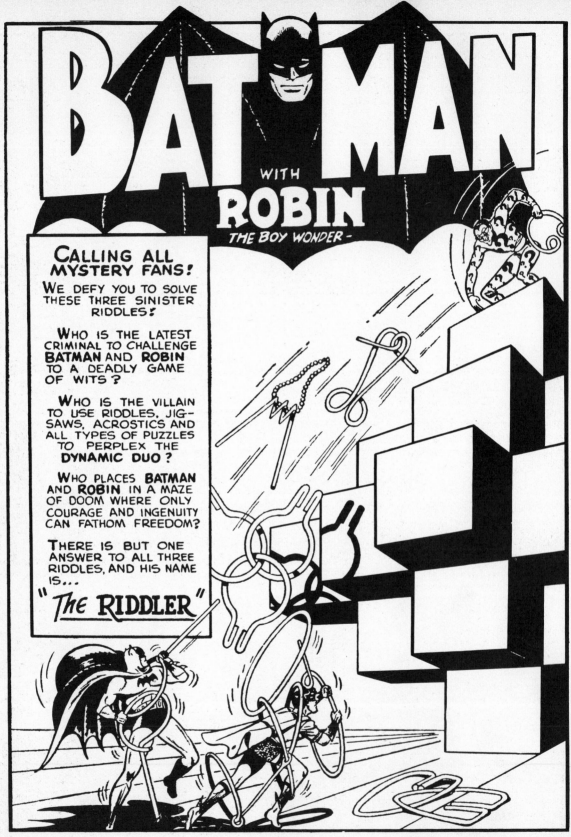

BAT MAN

WITH ROBIN THE BOY WONDER —

CALLING ALL MYSTERY FANS!

WE DEFY YOU TO SOLVE THESE THREE SINISTER RIDDLES!

WHO IS THE LATEST CRIMINAL TO CHALLENGE **BATMAN** AND **ROBIN** TO A DEADLY GAME OF WITS?

WHO IS THE VILLAIN TO USE RIDDLES, JIG-SAWS, ACROSTICS AND ALL TYPES OF PUZZLES TO PERPLEX THE **DYNAMIC DUO**?

WHO PLACES **BATMAN** AND **ROBIN** IN A MAZE OF DOOM WHERE ONLY COURAGE AND INGENUITY CAN FATHOM FREEDOM?

THERE IS BUT ONE ANSWER TO ALL THREE RIDDLES, AND HIS NAME IS...

"The RIDDLER"

THE CAREER OF THE RIDDLER BEGAN YEARS AGO, WITH A SCHOOL HISTORY CONTEST!

TOMORROW, EACH OF YOU WILL RECEIVE A DISASSEMBLED JIGSAW PUZZLE. THE FIRST TO PUT IT TOGETHER WINS A PRIZE!

I OUGHT TO WIN SURE! AFTER ALL, MY NAME'S EDWARD NIGMA— E. NIGMA!

BUT AFTER SCHOOL HOURS, THE BOY SECRETLY, JIMMIED OPEN HIS TEACHER'S DESK...

SO THAT'S WHAT THE COMPLETED PUZZLE LOOKS LIKE—COLUMBUS DISCOVERING AMERICA! I'LL TAKE A PICTURE OF IT WITH MY FLASH CAMERA!

AND NEXT DAY...

EDWARD NIGMA WAS THE FIRST TO SOLVE THE JIGSAW! HE WINS THE PRIZE!

PUZZLES ARE OKAY! I'M GOING TO LEARN HOW TO SOLVE ALL KINDS!

E. NIGMA SOON BECAME KNOWN AS A PUZZLE EXPERT AMONG HIS FRIENDS — WHO DIDN'T KNOW THAT HE CHEATED.

I KNEW YOU COULDN'T SOLVE THAT BENT-NAIL PUZZLE IN FIVE MINUTES!

LET'S SEE YOU DO IT!

PALMING THE PUZZLE WHICH HE'D PREVIOUSLY FIXED SO IT WAS *IMPOSSIBLE* TO OPEN, E. NIGMA SUBSTITUTED A *REGULAR* PUZZLE FOR IT, AND...

SEE... *OPEN!*

WOW! YOUR NAME SURE FITS YOU!

FIXED PUZZLE

THE BOY WHO CHEATED ON PUZZLES GREW TO BE A PUZZLE EXPERT... AND STILL CHEATED!

SOLVE THAT CHINESE PUZZLE AND I PAY YOU! IF YOU DON'T AND I DO... THEN YOU PAY ME!

...CH WITS WITH E. NIGMA THE PUZZLE KIN...

I'LL TRY IT!

OF COURSE I WIN AGAIN— SINCE I HAVE EACH PIECE MARKED WITH AN INVISIBLE INK WHICH SHOWS UP ONLY WHEN VIEWED THROUGH MY DARK GLASSES!

BUT THE SMALL PICKINGS OF A CARNIVAL ATTRACTION DO NOT SATISFY THE CROOKED PUZZLE MASTER!

I'M CLEVER ENOUGH AT PUZZLES TO BAFFLE EVEN THE POLICE—YES, AND BATMAN, TOO! WHY DON'T I COMMIT PUZZLING CRIMES?

I'LL MAKE EACH CRIME A DUEL OF WITS BETWEEN MYSELF AND THE LAW—AND FIX THE PUZZLES SO I'LL ALWAYS WIN! BUT FIRST I'LL NEED AN APPROPRIATE COSTUME—

SO IS BORN ONE OF THE STRANGEST OF PUBLIC ENEMIES, THE DANGEROUS, TRICKY CRIMINAL KNOWN AS—

THE RIDDLER! THAT'S WHAT I'LL CALL MYSELF— FOR THAT'S WHAT I'LL BE TO THE BATMAN!

THAT NIGHT, AS A CROWD WATCHES GOTHAM CITY'S NEWEST AND CLEVEREST ADVERTISING SIGN...

The CROSS CLEANING CO. PRESENTS ITS NIGHTLY CROSSWORD PUZZLE FOR YOUR ENTERTAINMENT!

WHILE IN THE SIGN'S CONTROL ROOM...

NO. 1 HORIZONTAL— A WINGLESS AUSTRALIAN BIRD

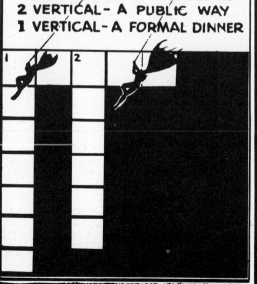

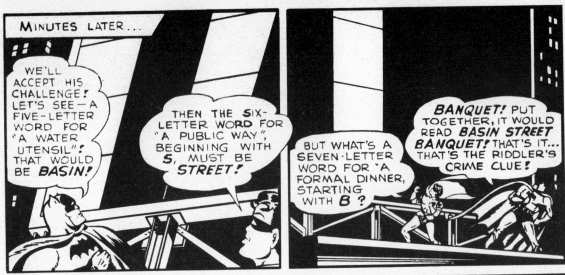

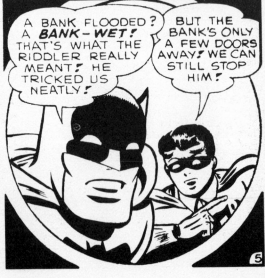

93

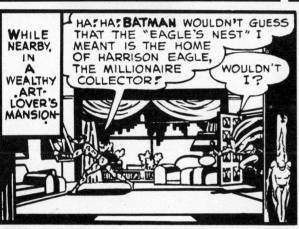

BY THE TIME THE DENSE SMOKE CLEARS...

THE RIDDLER WILL GET AWAY — AND I CAN'T FOLLOW HIM, KNOWING EAGLE WILL SUFFOCATE INSIDE THAT PUZZLE!

NOW BATMAN MATCHES HIS WITS AGAINST A HIGHLY COMPLEX PUZZLE, WITH A LIFE AT STAKE IF HE FAILS!

I'LL NEVER FIND THE SECRET OF THIS PUZZLE IN TIME TO SAVE HIM!

WAIT! THE LITTLE NICKS ON SOME OF THESE STEEL RODS WERE OBVIOUSLY MADE WHEN THE RODS SCRAPED AGAINST EACH OTHER!

BY CAREFULLY FOLLOWING THE TINY NICKS SHOWING HOW THE RODS WERE FITTED TOGETHER, BATMAN UNDOES THE PUZZLE!

JUST IN TIME, TOO!

UHHH!

AFTERWARDS... IT IS A GRIM BATMAN WHO REJOINS ROBIN!

THE RIDDLER'S STAGING A CRIME-CHARADE IN THIS TOWN THAT WE'VE GOT TO STOP! THAT MAN'S DANGEROUS!

MEANWHILE...

THAT WILL DO NICELY FOR MY FINAL CHALLENGE TO BATMAN AND ROBIN — A RIDDLE TO RID ME OF THEM — FOR GOOD!

HIGGINS CANNED CORN

NEXT MORNING, A DRIVERLESS TRUCK HURTLES WILDLY DOWN A GOTHAM CITY STREET WITH AN AMAZING CHALLENGE!

WE'LL BE KILLED!

DEAR BATMAN: HERE'S A CORNY RIDDLE TO TIP YOU OFF TO MY NEXT JOB. WHY IS CORN HARD TO ESCAPE FROM? — THE Riddler.

SUDDENLY, SOMETHING CUTS OFF THE CAREENING JUGGERNAUT — IT'S THE BATMOBILE!

THE RIDDLER DOESN'T CARE IF PEOPLE ARE KILLED — SO LONG AS HE HAS HIS FUN!

HMM! CORN SUGGESTS CORNMEAL, BAD JOKES, MAIZE —

MAIZE — ANOTHER NAME FOR CORN! A MAZE IS HARD TO ESCAPE FROM! AND THERE'S A BIG GLASS FUN MAZE OUT AT PLEASURE PIER AMUSEMENT PARK!

DEAR BATMAN: HERE'S A CORNY RIDDLE TO TIP YOU OFF TO MY NEXT JOB: WHY IS CORN HARD TO ESCAPE FROM? — THE Riddler.

AT THE AMUSEMENT PIER...

I'LL TAKE YOUR RECEIPTS, BY MEANS OF AN ACROSTIC! A-CROSS-STICK, TO YOU!

HELP! POLICE!

ABRUPTLY...

THERE HE GOES... INTO THE MAZE!

IF YOU WANT ME — COME AND GET ME!

FUN MAZE

WE'VE GOT ONE CHANCE—BUT IT'S A LONG ONE! GATHER UP THIS CARPET FROM THE FLOOR... AND PILE IT AGAINST THIS PANEL!

WHA...??

THEN **BATMAN** SCRAPES A MATCH...

FIRE WON'T CRACK OPEN THIS SHATTER-PROOF GLASS!

NO, BUT HEAT EXPANDS METAL MORE THAN IT DOES GLASS! IF IT EXPANDS THE METAL FRAME JUST ENOUGH—

—WE CAN PUSH ONE PANE OUT OF ITS LOOSENED METAL FRAME—LIKE THIS!

THEY GOT OUT!

DOWN, **ROBIN!** THAT BOMB IS DUE TO GO OFF!

HELP! I'M TRAPPED OUT HERE AT THE END OF THE PIER!

I'VE LOST... I'VE LOST THE GAME! YA-AA-AA!

MOMENTS LATER...

LOOK! A *QUESTION MARK* THAT CAME OFF THE RIDDLER'S COSTUME WHEN HE DROWNED!

OR PERHAPS HE ESCAPED DROWNING AND LEFT IT THERE TO PUZZLE US! ONLY TIME WILL SOLVE *THAT* RIDDLE!

THE END

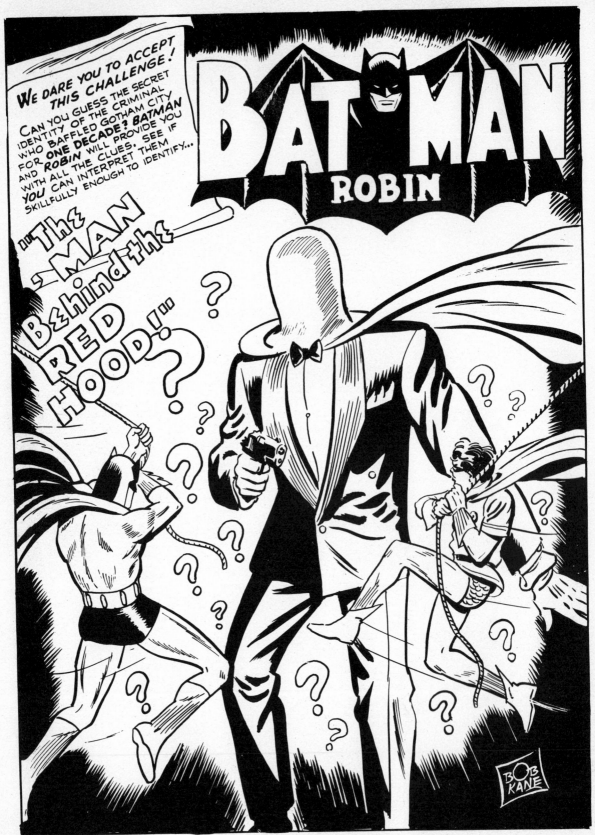

100

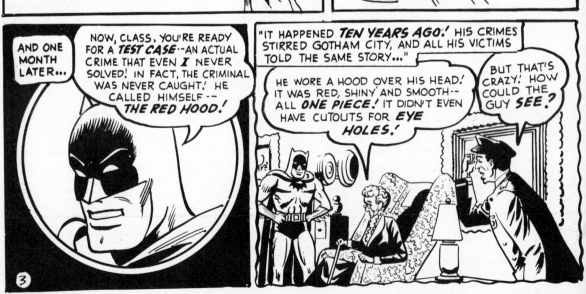

103

© 1954 National Comics Publications, Inc.

119

"MY IDEA WAS TO MINGLE WITH THE INDIANS AS ONE OF THEM, OPERATING FROM A BASE NEARBY. LUCKILY, I DISCOVERED MY **BAT-CAVE**-- IT WAS THE PERFECT SPOT..."

A RED STAIN, BREWED FROM TREE BARK. IT COLORS MY SKIN PERFECTLY FOR MY ROLE AS AN INDIAN!

"I HAD NO TROUBLE MINGLING WITH THE INDIANS. IN A TIME OF UPRISING, MANY TRIBES ALLY AND MIX. NEW FACES ARE NOT UNCOMMON..."

THE ALGONQUINS AND THE HURONS HAVE JUST ARRIVED! I MUST GET THIS INFORMATION TO CAPTAIN BOOTH AT FORT GEORGE!

"MY OPERATION WAS SUCCESSFUL. THE INDIAN ATTACKS WERE BEATEN OFF ONE BY ONE! BUT SOON THE OLD CHIEFS KNEW THERE MUST BE A SPY IN THEIR MIDST!"

THEY'RE TELLING THE MEDICINE MAN HIS MEDICINE IS BAD...HE MUST FIND THE SPY IN THE CAMP! I'D BEST BE EXTRA CAREFUL!

I WASN'T CAUGHT. I MADE MY REPORT TO FORT GEORGE, THEN STARTED BACK HERE. UNLUCKILY, I RAN INTO THOSE INDIANS -- BUT I'M SURE THEY DIDN'T KNOW WHO I REALLY WAS...

YOU'D BETTER REST NOW. I'VE SET YOUR LEG IN A SPLINT. WE'LL SEE THAT YOU GET WHAT YOU NEED.

BUT NOW--JUST WHEN MY ESPIONAGE IS NEEDED MOST--I'M HELPLESS! THE INDIANS ARE PLANNING A MAJOR CAMPAIGN-- AND I'M UNABLE TO SPY ON THEM! AND THE FATE OF THE WHOLE COLONY IS IN THE BALANCE!

DON'T BE TOO DISCOURAGED! PERHAPS THERE'S A WAY. MAYBE I COULD TAKE OVER FOR YOU, AFTER I'VE CHANGED A FEW THINGS AROUND HERE...

I NOTICE YOU LEAVE YOUR HORSE UNATTENDED WHILE YOU'RE DOWN HERE -- WHISTLING FOR HIM, WHEN YOU COME UP. THAT'S BAD-- THE ANIMAL **COULD** LEAD THE INDIANS TO THIS CAVE. COME ON, **ROBIN**-- WE'VE GOT WORK TO DO — IN THAT LOG-CABIN I SPOTTED BEFORE!

SOON AFTER, IN THE ABANDONED LOG CABIN ABOVE THE *BAT-CAVE*...

A FEW OF THE CONCENTRATED *EXPLOSIVE PILLS* FROM MY UTILITY BELT SHOULD BE ENOUGH TO BLOW A HOLE THROUGH TO THE *BAT-CAVE*..

AND WITH THIS VINE AND ALL THE TIMBER LYING AROUND, WE'LL RIG UP A REAL SURPRISE FOR JEREMY COE...

A FEW HOURS LATER, AS *BATMAN* AND *ROBIN* COMPLETE THEIR LABORS...

SHADES OF THE *WINCH* IN THE REAL *BAT-CAVE*!

THERE YOU ARE, COE! YOU RIDE YOUR HORSE INTO THE CABIN, THEN YOU COME DOWN HERE, AND PULL YOUR HORSE DOWN AFTER YOU!

WELL, I SWAN!

SOON AFTER...

WHAT ARE YOU DOING WITH THAT BIRCH-BARK? LOOKS LIKE SOME SORT OF PIPE...

YOU'LL SEE! I NOTICE YOU HAVE SOME HAND-MIRRORS, THE KIND INDIANS USE TO FLASH SIGNALS WITH SUNLIGHT. *ROBIN*, WOULD YOU GO GET THEM...?

THE WHOLE FLOOR OF THE CABIN COMES DOWN, COE. YOU JUST HAVE TO LEARN HOW TO HANDLE THESE ROPES MADE OF VINE!

SHORTLY AFTERWARDS...

IT'S CALLED A PERISCOPE, COE. BY RAISING IT THROUGH ITS OPENING IN THE CEILING, AND TWISTING IT AROUND, YOU'LL BE ABLE TO SEE IN ALL DIRECTIONS, AND POSSIBLY SPOT AN ATTACK ON THIS CAVE!

NOT EXACTLY AN ELECTRONIC WARNING DEVICE, NOR TELEVISION, BUT THOSE THINGS HAVEN'T BEEN INVENTED YET!

!!!

AND AS *BATMAN* CONTINUES "REARRANGING" THE OLD *BAT-CAVE*..

YOU USE A DYE MADE FROM BARK TO COLOR YOUR SKIN, BUT THERE'S MUCH MORE YOU CAN DO. THESE DIFFERENT SPECIES OF BARK, LEAVES AND HERBS CAN PROVIDE MEDICINES, TANNING AGENTS, CHEMICALS-- A WHOLE VARIETY OF THINGS!

THE CRIME LAB-- FRONTIER STYLE!

!!!

THEN...

DON'T YOU THINK IT WOULD BE A NICE IDEA TO START A TROPHY COLLECTION? HERE-- THE BOW-AND-ARROW USED BY THE INDIAN *ROBIN* WAS FIGHTING-- THAT'S A GOOD BEGINNING!

I WAS WONDERING IF *BATMAN* WOULD FORGET THE HALL OF TROPHIES! THAT'S A REAL UNUSUAL ARROW-HEAD-- IT WOULD GRACE *ANY* COLLECTION!

BOW AND ARROW TAKEN IN FIGHT WITH HURON INDIANS!

9

123

BATMAN IN THE 50s

IN **METROPOLIS CITY HALL**, ONE MORNING, A STARTLING SIGHT AROUSES A CLERK IN THE **LICENSES OFFICE**...

WH--WHY... YOU'RE **LUTHOR**, THE NOTORIOUS CRIMINAL-SCIENTIST! **YOU** WANT A MANUFACTURING LICENSE?

YES, I'VE SERVED MY TERM AND AM GOING TO USE MY SCIENTIFIC GENIUS AS AN HONEST BUSINESSMAN!

MY PARTNER WILL SIGN HIS NAME, TOO... **THE JOKER!**

YES, HA--HA-- I, TOO, AM GOING HONEST! I CAME HERE FROM GOTHAM CITY, TO GET A NEW START!

IT DOESN'T TAKE LONG FOR SENSATIONAL NEWS LIKE THIS TO REACH THE **DAILY PLANET**...

GREAT CAESAR'S GHOST! OUR CITY HALL REPORTER PHONED THAT **LUTHOR** AND **THE JOKER** ARE THERE TOGETHER, RIGHT NOW!

WOW-- HEAR THAT, CLARK? LET'S GO...

WHEN REPORTERS CLARK KENT AND LOIS LANE REACH THE SCENE...

WE'VE NOTHING TO HIDE, NOW THAT WE'RE GOING STRAIGHT! THIS AFTERNOON, WE'LL DEMONSTRATE THE NEW INVENTION WE'RE GOING TO MANUFACTURE, OUTSIDE OUR FACTORY!

YOU AND **THE JOKER** IN BUSINESS? THIS I'LL HAVE TO SEE!

BUT AS **THE JOKER'S** FLASHY CAR, THE **JOKERMOBILE**, ROLLS AWAY...

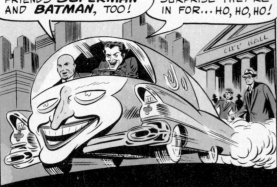

I'M SURE OUR NEW CAREERS WILL INTEREST OUR OLD FRIENDS **SUPERMAN** AND **BATMAN**, TOO!

YES-- HA, HA-- AND WHAT A SURPRISE THEY'RE IN FOR... HO, HO, HO!

AREN'T YOU COMING WITH ME, CLARK?

SORRY, LOIS, I... ER... JUST REMEMBERED ANOTHER ASSIGNMENT!

I HEARD WHAT **THE JOKER** SAID, WITH MY **SUPER-HEARING**! I DON'T LIKE THE SOUND OF THAT AT ALL!

GOOD... THAT'LL KEEP HER OUT OF TROUBLE! OF COURSE, IT WASN'T REALLY HER FAULT...THE *MECHANO-MEN* FOOLED US, TOO!

LUTHOR'S INGENIOUS INVENTION, AND *THE JOKER'S* WARPED SENSE OF HUMOR, ARE MAKING US *ALL* LOOK A BIT FOOLISH!

THEY MUST BE PULLING THESE TRICKS SO WE WON'T BOTHER THEM ANY MORE... THEN THEY CAN TRY A BIG CRIME!

BUT WHAT ARE THEY PLANNING? IF I COULD SEE INSIDE THEIR FACTORY, I MIGHT FIND OUT... BUT I CAN'T!

MAYBE YOU CAN, *SUPERMAN*... I JUST GOT AN IDEA! THOSE TWO WOULDN'T ALLOW US PAST THE DOOR OF THEIR FACTORY... BUT WHAT ABOUT WEALTHY *BRUCE WAYNE?* THEY'VE NO REASON TO SUSPECT *HIM!*

THUS A LITTLE LATER, IN THE FACTORY'S WEIRD OFFICE...

HA, HA... WE'VE MADE *SUPERMAN* AND *BATMAN* LOOK UTTERLY RIDICULOUS! AND THEY DON'T KNOW THE *REAL* JOKE ON THEM IS YET TO COME... HA, HA, HA!

QUIET, *JOKER*-- WE HAVE A CALLER!

AND AS THAT "CALLER" STATES HIS "BUSINESS"...

I'M BRUCE WAYNE, A DIRECTOR OF THE *WAYNE MINING COMPANY!* I READ OF YOUR NEW *MECHANO-MEN*, AND WOULD LIKE TO HIRE THEM FOR A TOUGH JOB!

WE DON'T PLAN TO RENT THEM OUT UNTIL AFTER TOMORROW'S BIG PUBLIC SHOWING OF THEIR ABILITIES!

TOO BAD... WHEN A MINING-BARGE SANK OFFSHORE RECENTLY, WE LOST SOME VALUABLE INDUSTRIAL DIAMONDS! HUMAN DIVERS CAN'T GO THAT DEEP!

OH...WELL--ER--SHOW ME THE LOCATION! WHEN WE OPEN OUR BUSINESS, WE'LL HAVE OUR *MECHANO-MEN* RECOVER THEM FOR YOU!

8

ONE NIGHT, IN THE HIDEOUT OF THE *JOKER*, THAT FANTASTIC CLOWN OF CRIME...

THREE WEEKS...AND NO SUCCESSES! COULD IT BE I'M GOING STALE?

THE BOSS IS IN A BAD WAY! HE HASN'T BEEN ABLE TO DREAM UP A GOOD CRIME LATELY!

TELEVISION, RADIO, MOVIE COMICS -- *BAH!* NONE OF THEM IS MY EQUAL AS A CLOWN--YET *THEY* NEVER SEEM TO RUN OUT OF IDEAS!!

SUDDENLY, A REALIZATION DAWNS ON THE *JOKER*...

OF COURSE! THESE COMICS NEVER RUN OUT OF MATERIAL BECAUSE THEY PAY GOOD MONEY *TO GET IT!* THEY USE *GAG WRITERS!*

WHAT DO YOU MEAN, JOKER?

SMACK!

IT'S A SPECIAL PROFESSION--WRITERS WHO DO NOTHING ELSE BUT COIN HUMOR! I'LL SHOW YOU WHAT I MEAN TOMORROW! *HA-HA!* IT'S GIVING ME A WONDERFUL IDEA!

NEXT DAY, AS THE *JOKER* AND HIS MEN POSE AS WINDOW WASHERS AT A RADIO STUDIO...

ALL RIGHT--LET'S HEAR THE GAGS YOU'VE GOT FOR MY SHOW NEXT WEEK! C'MON, NOW-- I NEED SOME GOOD ONES!

(WHISPER) THAT'S MARV BLACK, THE FAMOUS RADIO COMEDIAN. HE PAYS THOSE WRITERS A FORTUNE TO MAKE HIM SOUND FUNNY ON THE AIR!

WE'VE GOT A BASEBALL ROUTINE FIGURED OUT FOR YOU, MARV-- WAIT TILL YOU HEAR IT!

HA-HA! WHAT THESE COMICS DO, I-- *THE JOKER*-- CAN DO, TOO! I SHALL HIRE *GAG WRITERS* --TO DREAM UP CRIMES FOR ME! *HA-HA!*

2

SOON, THE WORD SPREADS THROUGH THE UNDERWORLD...

HEY, MUGGSY --THE JOKER'S LOOKING FER GUYS WHO KIN DREAM UP SCHEMES FOR HIS CRIMES.

SAAY-- THAT'S RIGHT DOWN MY ALLEY! JOKER --HERE I COME!

LISTEN! THERE'S A FORTUNE WAITIN' FOR THE GUY WHO CAN SUPPLY THE JOKER WITH SOME GOOD CRIME GIMMICKS!

WHAT ARE WE WAITIN' FOR --LET'S GO!

AND, AT A SPECIAL MEETING PLACE...

I GOT A MILLION OF 'EM, JOKER--A MILLION OF 'EM!

WAIT! WAIT! I WARN YOU --PLAIN GAGS AREN'T ENOUGH! I WANT CRIMES THAT WILL MAKE A FOOL OUT OF BATMAN! HA-HA!

GET A LOAD OF WHAT I GOT FOR YA, JOKER!

MAKE A FOOL OUT OF BATMAN! BOY-- YOU'RE SURE ASKIN' FOR PLENTY, JOKER!

I KNOW IT'S A TOUGH ASSIGNMENT--BUT I'M READY TO PAY HANDSOMELY FOR MY CRIMES! HA-HA! HO-HO!

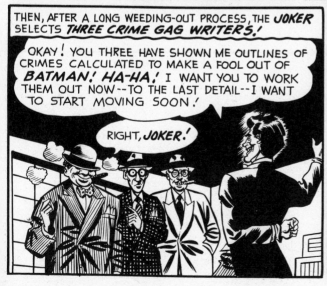

THEN, AFTER A LONG WEEDING-OUT PROCESS, THE JOKER SELECTS THREE CRIME GAG WRITERS!

OKAY! YOU THREE HAVE SHOWN ME OUTLINES OF CRIMES CALCULATED TO MAKE A FOOL OUT OF BATMAN! HA-HA! I WANT YOU TO WORK THEM OUT NOW --TO THE LAST DETAIL--I WANT TO START MOVING SOON!

RIGHT, JOKER!

WE'LL TRY YOURS FIRST, DOOLY! HO-HO! JUST THINKING ABOUT IT TICKLES ME! HA-HA! IMAGINE! WE'RE REALLY GOING TO LEAVE BATMAN HOLDING THE BAG!

HO! HA HA HO HA! HA!

③

A WEEK LATER, IN THE HOME OF BRUCE WAYNE AND HIS WARD, DICK GRAYSON...

OH-OH! I SEE THE PARADE TO THE FAIR HAS ALREADY BEGUN. WHAT DO YOU SAY WE GO OUT AND SEE THE FAIR IN PERSON, DICK?

A WONDERFUL IDEA--LET'S GO!

BUT, ALL AT ONCE...

WAIT A MINUTE! THERE GOES THE BAT-SIGNAL! LOOKS LIKE IT CHANGES OUR PLANS!

WELL, THE FAIR CAN WAIT! WE'VE GOT MORE IMPORTANT THINGS TO DO --AS BATMAN AND ROBIN!

SHORTLY AFTERWARDS, AT POLICE HEADQUARTERS...

TROUBLE, BOYS! THE JOKER AGAIN! HE'S TAUNTING US WITH THREATS TO ROB THE FAIR!

LOOKS LIKE WE'LL SEE THE FAIR AFTER ALL, ROBIN!

MEANWHILE...

HA-HA! CLEVER, DOOLY-- THIS METHOD OF GAINING ENTRANCE TO THE FAIR! IN A MOMENT, WE'LL BE READY TO GRAB THE GATE RECEIPTS!

RIGHT, JOKER! MY PLAN IS WORKING PERFECTLY! WAIT TILL BATMAN FALLS INTO THE TRAP! HA-HA!

NORTHERN STATE POTATOES

MOMENTS LATER...

HELP! THE JOKER! IT'S A ROBBERY!

THAT'S OUR CUE, ROBIN!

LOOK, ROBIN-- THEY'RE TRYING TO HIDE IN THAT BAG ON THE POTATO FLOAT! OR ARE THEY??

THEY'RE UP TO SOMETHING STRANGE, THAT'S FOR SURE!

AND INSIDE THE BAG...

HURRY UP, DOOLY--WE'RE READY TO PULL OUT!

HO-HO! WE PARKED OVER A MAN-HOLE--WE GO THROUGH THE TRAP DOOR TO FREEDOM --AND *BATMAN* IS LEFT HOLDING THE BAG! *HO-HO-HO!*

BUT THEY'RE IN THIS BAG!!

I DOUBT IT! IT'S JUST A RUSE! I THINK WE'LL FIND MORE IF WE'LL LOOK *UNDER* THIS FLOAT! IT'S PARKED OVER A SEWER MANHOLE!

AND AS THE LAWMEN SWIFTLY CAST ASIDE THE UNDERPINNING OF THE FLOAT...

JUST AS I THOUGHT! NOT SO FAST, MY FRIEND!

WE'VE GOT ONE OF THEM ANYWAY--AND WE'VE GOT THE LOOT!

THAT EVENING...

GOTHAM GAZETTE

JOKER ESCAPES CAPTURE; BATMAN LEFT HOLDING BAG

BUT CRIME CLOWN'S TRIUMPH IS MARRED WHEN HENCHMAN IS SEIZED WITH STOLEN MONEY.

AND, AT THE *JOKER'S* HIDEOUT...

DOOLY, BAH! HE *RUINED* HIS OWN SCHEME WITH HIS SLOWNESS! HIBBS--I'LL TRY YOUR *CRIME GAG* NEXT--AND IT BETTER BE MORE SUCCESSFUL!

RIGHT, BOSS...

IT'S BEEN A BAD DAY! BUT YOU CAN SAVE EVERY-THING, HIBBS! YOU SAY YOU CAN MAKE *JACKASSES* OUT OF *BATMAN* AND *ROBIN!* *HO-HO!* THAT WILL BE TERRIFIC!

AND HOW, BOSS! AND I CAN'T MISS, I TELL YA!

AND AS THE LAWMEN MAKE THEIR WAY OUT OF THE BLAZING BUILDING...

ROBIN, LISTEN! THE JOKER WOULDN'T MISS OUR APPEARANCE IN THESE COSTUMES FOR ANYTHING! KEEP YOUR EYES PEELED WHEN WE GET OUT!

RIGHT!

LOOK! BATMAN AND ROBIN -- A COUPLE OF JACKASSES! THE JOKER MADE HIS BOAST GOOD!

ROBIN -- I WAS RIGHT! THERE'S THE JOKER -- ON THE ROOF ACROSS THE STREET! LET'S MOVE!

MOVING LIKE THE WIND, THE DYNAMIC DUO RACES TO THE ROOF. IN HIS HASTE TO ESCAPE, HIBBS STUMBLES!

TOO LATE TO GET THE JOKER -- WE'LL HAVE TO SETTLE FOR THIS CHARACTER!

AND DON'T FORGET THE LOOT! WE'VE SAVED IT AGAIN!

NEXT DAY...

GOTHAM GAZETTE

JOKER MAKES JACKASS OUT OF BATMAN AND ROBIN!

BUT LAWMEN AGAIN HAVE LAST LAUGH BY RECOVERING LOOT OF LATEST THEFT!

BATMAN AND ROBIN

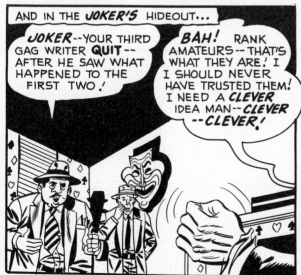

AND IN THE JOKER'S HIDEOUT...

JOKER -- YOUR THIRD GAG WRITER QUIT -- AFTER HE SAW WHAT HAPPENED TO THE FIRST TWO!

BAH! RANK AMATEURS -- THAT'S WHAT THEY ARE! I SHOULD NEVER HAVE TRUSTED THEM! I NEED A CLEVER IDEA MAN -- CLEVER -- CLEVER!

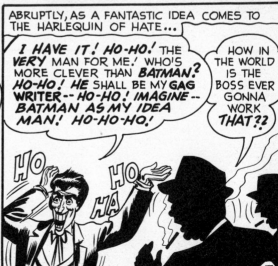

ABRUPTLY, AS A FANTASTIC IDEA COMES TO THE HARLEQUIN OF HATE...

I HAVE IT! HO-HO! THE VERY MAN FOR ME! WHO'S MORE CLEVER THAN BATMAN? HO-HO! HE SHALL BE MY GAG WRITER -- HO-HO! IMAGINE -- BATMAN AS MY IDEA MAN! HO-HO-HO!

HOW IN THE WORLD IS THE BOSS EVER GONNA WORK THAT??

HO HO HA HO HO HA

7

NEXT DAY, A STRANGE AD RUNS IN A GOTHAM CITY PAPER...

NOTICE!!

TO ALL PROSPECTIVE CRIME GAG WRITERS SEEKING EMPLOYMENT WITH THE JOKER: MY OFFER OF EMPLOYMENT IS NOW WITHDRAWN, BECAUSE THE JOB WILL SOON BE FILLED BY AN EXTREMELY CAPABLE PERSON. THANK YOU FOR SHOWING AN INTEREST IN MY PROJECT--BUT I HAVE FOUND THE IDEAL MAN FOR MY PURPOSES! HIS NAME IS --
BATMAN! HA-HA!
THE JOKER

AND AT POLICE HEAD-QUARTERS...

I DON'T LIKE THIS AT ALL! THE JOKER APPARENTLY HAS SOMETHING UP HIS SLEEVE IN HIS LATEST CAMPAIGN TO MAKE FOOLS OF YOU!

WELL--SO FAR HE'S FAILED-- WE'VE THWARTED HIS CRIMES! MAYBE NEXT TIME WE'LL CATCH HIM AND PUT AN END TO THIS!

A FEW NIGHTS LATER, AT THE GOTHAM STATE FAIR...

THE JOKER, BATMAN! HE'S GONE INTO THE TUNNEL OF LOVE!

YOU WATCH THE ENTRANCE, ROBIN! I'LL GET OVER TO THE EXIT, AND COME IN THAT WAY. AND BE CAREFUL--THIS COULD BE A TRAP!

MEANWHILE...

HA-HA! I THOUGHT THEY'D SPLIT UP! NOW FOR MY LITTLE GAME--QUICK, I MUST CHANGE MY UNIFORM!

NOW SHOWING

A MOMENT LATER...

BOO-HOO! BOO-HOO! MY BALLOON! THE WIND BLEW IT AWAY FROM ME! BOO-HOO! (SOB!)

DON'T CRY, SONNY--I'LL GET YOUR BALLOON BACK FOR YOU!

I KNOW HOW THAT POOR KID FEELS--IT'LL ONLY TAKE A SECOND FOR ME TO RETRIEVE HIS BALLOON...

THEN, AS THE BALLOON SCUDS AROUND A CORNER...

TRICKED-- BY THE JOKER!

YES! HA-HA! AN IMPER-SONATOR IN THE TUNNEL-- A MIDGET DRESSED UP A KID --AND THIS BALLOON ON THE END OF A STRING! HO-HO! I'VE GOT YOU NOW, ROBIN!

8

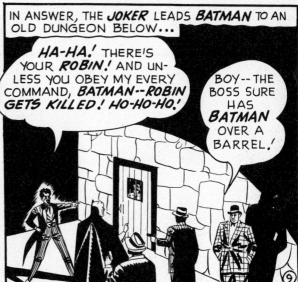

YEAH--I DID IT! I WANTED TO RUIN HIS HANDSOME MUG! EVER SINCE HE MET MY GIRL, SHE HASN'T LOOKED AT ME! SHE'LL NEVER MARRY HIM NOW!

YOU FOOL! BECAUSE OF YOUR JEALOUSY, YOU'VE DONE A TERRIBLE THING!

DAYS LATER, WHEN THE DOCTOR FINALLY UNWINDS THE BANDAGES...

UGGH! MY FACE! SCARRED ON ONE SIDE--JUST LIKE THE REAL TWO-FACE! I'M AS HIDEOUS AS TWO-FACE EVER WAS!

EASY, LAD! IT COULD HAVE BEEN WORSE! THE ACID MIGHT HAVE DESTROYED YOUR SIGHT!

MY ACTING CAREER IS FINISHED! THE ONLY ROLE I CAN EVER PLAY NOW IS TWO-FACE! AND I WON'T EVEN NEED ANY MAKEUP! THERE'S IRONY FOR YOU! PAUL SLOANE IS GONE--AND IN HIS PLACE STANDS TWO-FACE!

I HOPE THIS DOESN'T EFFECT HIS MIND! REMEMBER WHAT IT DID TO HARVEY DENT?

IT'S NATURAL THAT THE INITIAL SHOCK WILL MAKE HIM BITTER! LET HIM REST NOW--TOMORROW, I'LL TALK TO HIM OF PLASTIC SURGERY AGAIN!

BUT THE SHOCK HAS AFFECTED SLOANE'S MIND TO A GREATER DEGREE THAN IMAGINED...

MORONY'S SILVER DOLLAR! IT HAS TWO FACES--CLEAN AND HANDSOME AS MINE ONCE WERE! I'LL MAKE ONE OF ITS FACES UGLY, EVIL LIKE MINE!

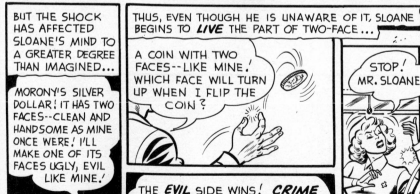

THUS, EVEN THOUGH HE IS UNAWARE OF IT, SLOANE BEGINS TO LIVE THE PART OF TWO-FACE...

A COIN WITH TWO FACES--LIKE MINE! WHICH FACE WILL TURN UP WHEN I FLIP THE COIN?

THE EVIL SIDE WINS! CRIME WINS! FROM THIS DAY ON, THIS TWO-FACED COIN WILL BE THE SYMBOL OF TWO-FACE!

STOP! MR. SLOANE...

MY NAME IS NOT SLOANE! I AM THE LIVING JEKYLL-HYDE--A MAN TO BE FEARED! FROM THIS DAY ON, THE WORLD WILL KNOW OF ME AND THE NEW CRIMES OF TWO-FACE!

ALMOST EXACTLY THE WORDS OF THE REAL TWO-FACE, LEARNED FROM THE TV SCRIPT HE HAD MEMORIZED!

3

RELIEVED BY *TWO-FACE'S* AGREEMENT, *BATMAN* AND *ROBIN* ARE CAUGHT OFF-GUARD BY A TREACHEROUS SURPRISE ATTACK!

YOU SHOULDN'T HAVE TRUSTED MY WORD! IT'S ONLY NATURAL *TWO-FACE* WOULD *DOUBLE-CROSS* YOU!

WHEN THE MANHUNTERS AWAKEN, IT IS THEY WHO ARE CAPTIVE...

A LOT O' GUYS IN PRISONS ARE GONNA BE GLAD WHEN THEY HEAR I KNOCKED OFF *BATMAN* AND *ROBIN!*

NO, BLINKY! MY *COIN* WILL DECIDE! IF THE GOOD SIDE COMES UP, THEY LIVE--BUT IF THE BAD SIDE COMES UP, THEY *DIE!*

THE COIN SPINS HIGH, DROPS INTO THE PALM--AND IN THAT PALM RESTS THE FATE OF *BATMAN* AND *ROBIN!*

AGH! THE *GOOD* SIDE WON! BUT YOU DOUBLE-CROSSED 'EM ONCE--WHY DON'T YA DOUBLE-CROSS 'EM AGAIN AND LET ME BUMP 'EM OFF ANYWAY?

TRUE, I'VE GONE BACK ON MY WORD--BUT *NEVER* AGAINST THE DECISION OF MY COIN! THAT COIN IS MY TRADE-MARK--THE SYMBOL OF *TWO-FACE!*

LATER...

THIS WAS OUR LUCKY DAY! BLINKY WOULD'VE SHOT US IF *TWO-FACE* HADN'T STUCK TO HIS COIN'S TOSS!

ROBIN, IT'S JUST POSSIBLE THAT COIN MAY HELP US END THIS ENTIRE CASE!

AS THEY RETURN TO HEADQUARTERS, THEY ARE MET BY AN OLD FRIEND--*HARVEY DENT,* THE EX-D.A. WHO WAS ONCE THE *ORIGINAL TWO-FACE!*

I WAS IN EUROPE WHEN I HEARD ABOUT POOR SLOANE! I JUST FLEW IN! WHAT CAN I DO TO HELP?

HARVEY, PERHAPS IF SLOANE COULD SEE AND LISTEN TO YOU, IT MIGHT BRING HIM TO HIS SENSES!

THAT VERY NIGHT, ALL TELEVISION NETWORKS ARE GIVEN OVER TO AN EMERGENCY BROADCAST...

SLOANE, WHEREVER YOU ARE, LISTEN TO ME! LOOK AT MY FACE! SEE HOW PLASTIC SURGERY RESTORED MY FEATURES! IT CAN BE THE SAME FOR YOU! YOU'LL BE PAUL SLOANE, THE HANDSOME ACTOR YOU ONCE WERE!

HIS FACE... THE WAY MINE USED TO BE... HANDSOME... UNSCARRED...

WILL THE PLEAS OF THE MAN WHO WAS ONCE TWO-FACE HELP REFORM THE SECOND TWO-FACE?

BUT THE BROADCAST HAS THE **REVERSE** EFFECT--FOR IT ONLY INFURIATES THE UNFORTUNATE MAN'S TWISTED THOUGHTS!

BAH! THEY DISGUISED AN ACTOR TO LOOK LIKE ME! THEY'RE TRYING TO **TRICK** ME! THERE IS ONLY **ONE** TWO-FACE-- AND I AM HIM!

THIS GUY'S NUTS, BUT AS LONG AS HE THINKS UP GOOD JOBS, I'M STICKIN' WITH HIM!

SMASH!

AND SO, **TWO-FACE** AGAIN TURNS TO HIS TRADE-MARK CRIMES, BASING ALL ON THE TOSS OF HIS TWO-FACED COIN!

THE BAD SIDE WINS!

A NICE HAUL OF PAID ADMISSIONS FOR A **DOUBLE-HEADER** GAME!

PARKING

TICKETS

DOUBLE HEADER BASEBALL GAME TODAY

AND WHEN THE SCARRED SIDE WINS AGAIN, A **DOUBLE-FEATURE** MOVIE HOUSE IS ROBBED!

BIG DOUBLE FEATU

SOON

ADMISSION

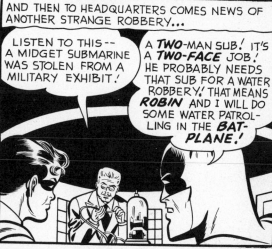

AND THEN TO HEADQUARTERS COMES NEWS OF ANOTHER STRANGE ROBBERY...

LISTEN TO THIS-- A MIDGET SUBMARINE WAS STOLEN FROM A MILITARY EXHIBIT!

A **TWO**-MAN SUB! IT'S A **TWO-FACE** JOB! HE PROBABLY NEEDS THAT SUB FOR A WATER ROBBERY! THAT MEANS **ROBIN** AND I WILL DO SOME WATER PATROL-LING IN THE **BAT-PLANE!**

AFTERWARD, FROM UNDER THE GOTHAM RIVER, A SUBMARINE PERISCOPE SCANS A SLOW-MOVING CRAFT.

I CAN SEE OUR QUARRY ON THE FERRY! PREPARE TO **SURFACE!**

MOMENTS LATER, AFTER GAINING THE FERRY...

YOU'RE PROFESSOR HODGE OF THE GOTHAM ZOO! YOU'RE CARRY-ING THE EGG OF AN AMAZON JUNGLE BIRD SO RARE IT'S NEVER BEEN BRED IN CAPTIVITY! I WANT THAT EGG!

B-BUT I'VE ONE **ONE** EGG! IT'S NOT LIKE YOU TO STEAL SOMETHING UNLESS **TWO** OF SOMETHING IS INVOLVED!

HOW CAN **TWO-FACE** STEAL A SINGLE EGG, AND YET FULFILL HIS THEME OF SYMBOLIC CRIMES ALWAYS BASED ON **TWO**? CAN YOU GUESS?

⑦

I'VE INSIDE INFORMATION FROM SOMEONE WHO *CANDLED* THAT EGG! THAT SINGLE EGG HAS A *DOUBLE-YOLK*-- WHICH MEANS IT WILL HATCH *TWO* RARE AND EXTREMELY VALUABLE BIRDS INSTEAD OF ONLY ONE!

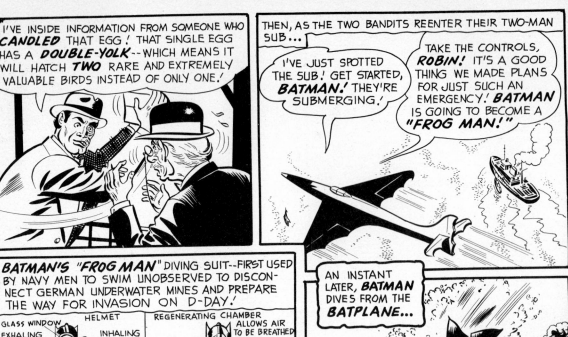

THEN, AS THE TWO BANDITS REENTER THEIR TWO-MAN SUB...

I'VE JUST SPOTTED THE SUB! GET STARTED, *BATMAN!* THEY'RE SUBMERGING!

TAKE THE CONTROLS, *ROBIN!* IT'S A GOOD THING WE MADE PLANS FOR JUST SUCH AN EMERGENCY! *BATMAN* IS GOING TO BECOME A *"FROG MAN!"*

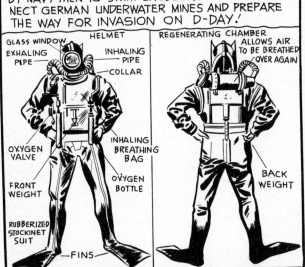

BATMAN'S "FROG MAN" DIVING SUIT--FIRST USED BY NAVY MEN TO SWIM UNOBSERVED TO DISCONNECT GERMAN UNDERWATER MINES AND PREPARE THE WAY FOR INVASION ON D-DAY!

GLASS WINDOW
EXHALING PIPE
HELMET
INHALING PIPE
COLLAR
OXYGEN VALVE
INHALING BREATHING BAG
FRONT WEIGHT
OXYGEN BOTTLE
RUBBERIZED STOCKINET SUIT
FINS

REGENERATING CHAMBER ALLOWS AIR TO BE BREATHED OVER AGAIN
BACK WEIGHT

AN INSTANT LATER, *BATMAN* DIVES FROM THE *BATPLANE...*

LIKE SOME BIZARRE UNDERWATER CREATURE, *BATMAN* MOVES UNDER THE SURFACE WITH THE WEB-FOOTED SURENESS OF A GIANT FROG!

NOW I'LL HITCH A RIDE AND LET THE SUB TAKE ME RIGHT TO *TWO-FACE'S* HIDEOUT!

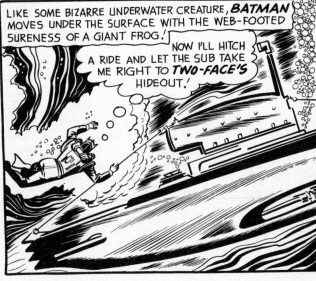

AND SO, BECAUSE *BATMAN* HAS *DOUBLED* AS A *"FROG MAN,"* HE FINALLY TRACKS DOWN THE LAIR OF *TWO-FACE!*

EVERYTHING ACCORDING TO PATTERN-- *TWO-FACE'S* HIDEOUT IS AN OLD *TWO-MASTED* SCHOONER!

8

LATER, AS BLINKY WALKS THE DECK ALONE, A FIST SEEMS TO COME OUT OF NOWHERE...

THAT TAKES CARE OF BLINKY! NOW I'LL TIE HIM UP AND HIDE HIM SOMEWHERE! MY PLAN WON'T WORK UNLESS I'M ALONE WITH *TWO-FACE!*

SMACK

SOON AFTER...

BATMAN! WHERE *YOU* COME FROM?

WHAT'S MORE IMPORTANT IS, WHERE YOU'RE GOING!

GRAPPLING LIKE SAVAGE CAVEMEN, THE TWO THRASH ABOUT THE CABIN FLOOR...

BUT *TWO-FACE* SEEMS TO GAIN THE ADVANTAGE, AND THEN...

HAH! YOUR STRENGTH IS GREATLY OVER-RATED, *BATMAN!*

SPLAT

AND SO, ONCE AGAIN *BATMAN'S* FATE RESTS ON THE TOSS OF A COIN!

WELL, *BATMAN*, WHAT SHALL IT BE THIS TIME? WILL YOU LIVE OR WILL YOU DIE? WILL THE GOOD SIDE OF THE COIN WIN OR WILL IT BE THE BAD SIDE?

WAIT! *WHAT IF THE COIN STANDS ON EDGE?*

9

WILL YOU AGREE TO GIVE YOURSELF UP AND SUBMIT TO PLASTIC SURGERY, *IF THE COIN STANDS ON EDGE?*

OF COURSE I AGREE TO WHAT-EVER THE COIN DE-CIDES -- BUT YOU'RE A FOOL! IT'S A MILLION-TO-ONE THAT THE COIN WILL *NEVER* STAND ON EDGE! HA! HA!

APPARENTLY, *BATMAN* HAS STAKED EVERY-THING ON A MILLION-TO-ONE CHANCE! WILL HE WIN--OR LOSE? WATCH THE SPINNING COIN!

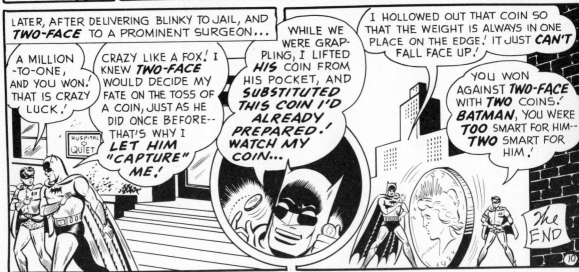

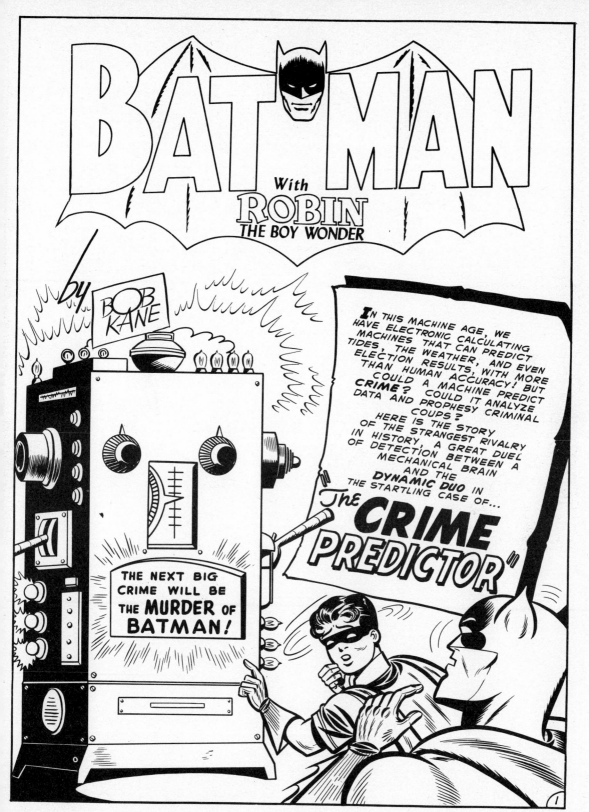

© 1953 National Comics Publications, Inc.

IN A LABORATORY ON THE OUTSKIRTS OF GOTHAM, DR. EDWARD ARVIN, A BRILLIANT SCIENTIST, PREPARES TO REVEAL AN AMAZING INVENTION TO THE CITY'S TOP LAWMEN...

MY *PREDICTOR* WORKS ON AN ELECTRONIC PRINCIPLE! WHEN I FEED CRIMINAL STATISTICS INTO IT ON TAPE, IT MATHEMATICALLY PREDICTS THE FUTURE ACTIONS OF ANY KNOWN CRIMINAL!

HMM! WELL, WE'D LIKE TO LAY OUR HANDS ON "MUGS" WILDEN... ASK IT WHAT *HE'S* GOING TO DO NEXT!

I'VE CALLED YOU HERE, GENTLEMEN, BECAUSE THIS MACHINE MUST BE KEPT SECRET. IF THE UNDERWORLD HEARS OF MY *CRIME PREDICTOR*, THEY'LL STOP AT NOTHING TO DESTROY IT!

GO AHEAD! AS LONG AS I'M POLICE COMMISSIONER, WE CAN'T AFFORD TO OVERLOOK ANY POSSIBLE *WEAPON* AGAINST CRIME!

POWER IS SWITCHED INTO THE GIANT CALCULATOR...AND THE UNCANNY ELECTRONIC BRAIN ANSWERS...

BY EVALUATING ITS INFORMATION ON WILDEN'S METHODS OF CRIME, AND THEN SELECTING FROM ITS DATA ON BANKS, PAYROLLS AND POSSIBLE LOOT, IT CAN MAKE THIS ACCURATE PREDICTION!

IT SEEMS TOO GOOD TO BE TRUE... HMM... I HAVE AN IDEA TO TEST IT.

ON THE SCREEN...

MUGS WILDEN WILL ROB GOTHAM BALLBEARING PAYROLL TOMORROW AT NINE A.M.!

DOCTOR, I MUST PROTECT MY IDENTITY... AND THIS MACHINE *MIGHT* EXPOSE IT! I WANT, IN PRIVACY, TO SEE IF IT CAN IDENTIFY ME!

I HADN'T THOUGHT OF THAT DANGER! OF COURSE, I'LL SHOW YOU HOW TO FEED QUESTIONS INTO IT ON PAPER TAPE, AND ONLY YOU WILL BE HERE TO KNOW THE ANSWER!

INSUFFICIENT...DATA... BUT MR. BLANK'S KNOWLEDGE OF CRIMINALS IMPLIES A LONG CRIMINAL RECORD!

AND, WHEN THE OTHERS HAVE STEPPED OUTSIDE, IN ANSWER TO THE QUESTION "WHO IS *BATMAN?*"...

BUT IT'S A LOGICAL GUESS! I'LL ASK IT, "WHO IS *MR. BLANK*, THE SECRET BOSS OF GOTHAM CITY?"

GOSH, *BATMAN*, THAT'S CLOSE... TOO CLOSE!

INSUFFICIENT DATA... BUT FACTS INDICATE BATMAN IS A RICH MAN, WITH NO JOB OR BUSINESS TO HAMPER HIS CAREER!

YES, BUT NOT VERY HELPFUL! *ROBIN*, TELL GORDON AND DR. ARVIN TO COME BACK IN... I'M GOING TO ASK THE MACHINE WHAT *MR. BLANK'S* NEXT CRIME WILL BE!

A LOGICAL ANSWER, TOO!

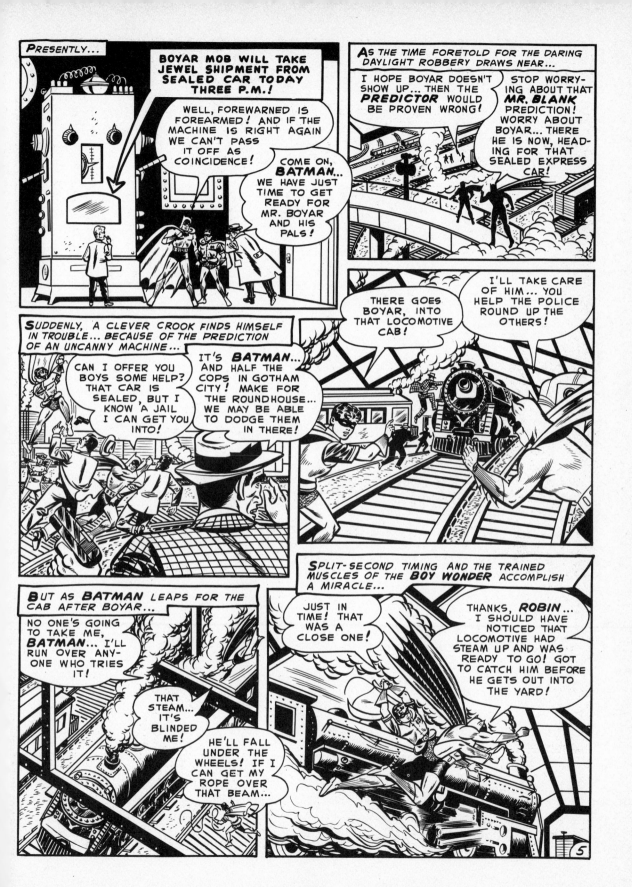

166

IN ANOTHER ROOM, USING HIS WIZARDRY OF MAKE-UP SKILL...

WHAT'S YOUR IDEA, *BATMAN?* ROBEY WON'T TALK ANY MORE ABOUT *MR. BLANK!*

NO, BUT MAYBE *MR. BLANK* HIMSELF WILL TALK...

... TO ROBEY... MEANING *ME!*

YOU'RE GOING TO PASS YOURSELF OFF AS ROBEY TO GET TO *MR. BLANK?* BATMAN, IT'S DANGEROUS IF HE SEES THROUGH YOUR DISGUISE!

FIRST I'LL SEARCH ROBEY'S BELONGINGS FOR A LEAD TO *MR. BLANK'S* BASE! YOU TAKE THE *REAL* ROBEY AND DELIVER HIM SECRETLY TO THE POLICE!

IF YOU SAY SO...BUT THAT PROPHECY OF THE PREDICTOR ABOUT *MR. BLANK* MURDERING YOU STILL WORRIES ME! BATMAN, REMEMBER THE PREDICTOR'S BEEN RIGHT EVERY TIME SO FAR!

WHEN *ROBIN* HAS LEFT WITH THE BOUND CRIMINAL, A CAREFUL SEARCH FINALLY REVEALS...

ROBEY WAS TOO SMART TO LEAVE ANYTHING WRITTEN DOWN! BUT THIS SMEAR ON HIS TOPCOAT... IT'S OF A SPECIAL DARK OIL! I'VE SEEN THIS OIL BEFORE... NOW I REMEMBER!

THIS SPECIAL OIL IS USED TO KEEP DEEP-SEA DIVERS' SUITS SUPPLE! DIVERS...SALVAGE... OF COURSE! A *SALVAGE COMPANY* WOULD MAKE AN IDEAL FRONT FOR A BIG-TIME CROOK TO USE IN SELLING STOLEN GOODS!

QUICKLY, THE DISGUISED *BATMAN* BEGINS TELEPHONING SALVAGE COMPANIES...

THIS IS ROG ROBEY SPEAKING! WHAT'S THE NEWS?

IF IT'S THE ONE I'M HUNTING, THEY'LL KNOW THAT NAME!

ROG ROBEY? DON'T KNOW THE NAME! YOU MUST HAVE THE WRONG COMPANY!

BUT THE THIRD SALVAGE COMPANY *BATMAN* CALLS...

ROBEY? WHY DON'T YOU GET DOWN HERE? YOU KNOW THE BOSS IS HOLDING A BIG ORGANIZING MEETING TONIGHT!

ROG ROBEY? DON'T KNOW THE NAME!

I KNOW! I'LL GET RIGHT DOWN! SO THE ACME SALVAGE COMPANY IS THE PLACE! AND IF I'M RIGHT, *MR. BLANK* IS THE BOSS HE MEANT! YES, I'LL BE AT THAT MEETING!

7

I WENT BACK AND WRECKED IT! AND WHEN I DID SO, I PICKED UP AN INTERESTING GUEST! BRING OUR "GUEST" OUT FOR THEM TO SEE, ROBEY!

BUT I'M ROBEY... UNLESS THIS MEANS...

BUT ROBEY'S ALREADY HERE! THERE'S TWO OF 'EM...

I FOUND THE REAL ROBEY TIED UP IN ROBIN'S BATMOBILE... AND THAT ROBEY IS BATMAN, IN DISGUISE! DON'T TRY ANYTHING, BATMAN, UNLESS YOU WANT YOUR YOUNG PAL TO GET HURT!

BATMAN AND ROBIN! LET'S DROP THEM IN THE SEA!

NO, WE'LL HANG 'EM...

THAT COMPRESSION-CHAMBER WILL FURNISH A MORE INTERESTING EXECUTION FOR THEM, AND ONE YOU'LL ALL ENJOY!

THAT CHAMBER'S USED TO KEEP DEEP-SEA DIVERS UNDER HIGH COMPRESSED-AIR PRESSURE WHEN THEY FIRST COME UP, SO THEY WON'T GET THE "BENDS"! WE'LL PUT THEM IN AND TURN ON THE PUMPS!

WHAT AN IDEA! WHEN WE SUDDENLY OPEN UP AND DROP THE PRESSURE ON THEM, THE SUDDEN DROP'LL KILL 'EM SLOW! SO WE CAN ALL ENJOY IT!

IT'S A SLIM CHANCE... BUT SOME OF THOSE CROOKS ARE SMOKING CIGARETTES, AND THAT'S OUR ONLY CHANCE!

GET IN THAT CHAMBER, YOU TWO!

PRESENTLY, AS THE CRIME-FIGHTERS ARE LOCKED INSIDE THE CHAMBER...

NO USE KEEPING THIS DISGUISE... IF WE GO OUT, IT'LL BE IN OUR OWN COSTUMES!

BATMAN, IT'S MY FAULT... I WAS WORRIED ABOUT THE PREDICTOR'S PROPHECY, AND THOUGHT THE MACHINE MIGHT HELP ME TO HELP YOU...

AS PUMPS BEGIN THROBBING OMINOUSLY, FORCING AIR INTO THE TANK...

THERE'S NO WAY OUT OF THIS ONE! BUT THAT IT SHOULD BE ME WHO HELPED THAT TERRIBLE PREDICTION TO COME TRUE!

WE'VE STILL ONE CHANCE! WITHOUT THEIR SEEING, I OPENED THE VALVES OF THOSE ACETYLENE TANKS THAT STOOD BEHIND US...

9

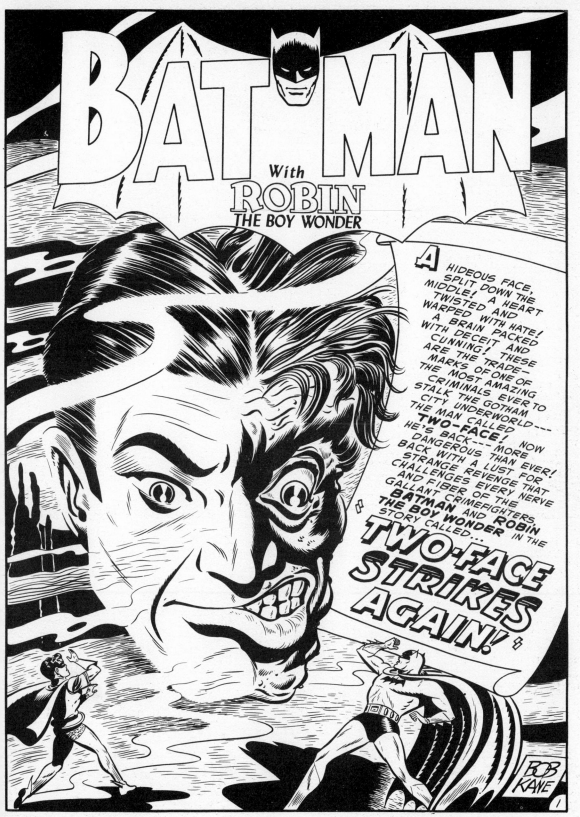

AND NOW IT BECOMES CLEAR THAT MORE THAN DENT'S FACE HAS BEEN RE-INJURED! THE SCAR REACHES RIGHT THROUGH TO HIS BRAIN!

THIS SETTLES IT! THIS **PROVES** I WAS **MEANT** TO BE A CRIMINAL! FATE HAS DECREED IT! MY DOCTOR WARNED ME AGAINST ANY FUTURE ACCIDENTS-- SAID PLASTIC SURGERY COULDN'T BE PERFORMED A SECOND TIME! I'M DOOMED TO LOOK THIS WAY FOR THE REST OF MY LIFE!

ALL RIGHT! IF THAT'S THE WAY IT MUST BE, I'LL GIVE IT THE FINAL TEST! I HAD A DUPLICATE MADE OF MY FAMED **TWO-FACED** COIN, TO KEEP AS A MEMENTO! I'LL SOON SEE IF ITS DECISION CONCURS WITH THAT OF FATE!

SOON AFTER...

AHHH-- HERE IT IS! ONE FACE OF THE COIN MARRED--- THE **EVIL** FACE! IF THAT COMES UP WHEN I SPIN THE COIN--THEN **BATMAN** AND **ROBIN** BEWARE!

ABRUPTLY, **TWO-FACE** FLIPS THE BIZARRE COIN INTO THE AIR, THEN, AS IT BOUNCES AND FINALLY SETTLES ON THE FLOOR--

THE **EVIL** FACE UP! THE CRIMINAL CAREER OF **TWO-FACE** BEGINS AGAIN! AND I MUST THINK UP SOMETHING **VERY SPECIAL** TO FIT THE OCCASION!

NEXT EVENING AT THE GOTHAM CITY CIRCUS, THE AUDIENCE GETS AN UNEXPECTED SHOCK...

LOOK! IT'S **TWO-FACE!** HE'S BACK IN OUR MIDST!

HE'S PROBABLY AFTER THE GATE RECEIPTS! CALL THE POLICE!

STILL USING HIS PERSONAL SYMBOL, THE NUMBER **TWO!** SEE? TWO WHITE HORSES! HELP!

BUT THE SCARRED CRIMINAL DOES NOT ATTACK THE BOXOFFICE, AS EXPECTED! INSTEAD, HE BARGES INTO THE DRESSING-ROOM OF TARANDO, WORLD-FAMOUS CLOWN!

AHH! TARANDO, THE CLOWN! KNOWN TO KEEP A FABULOUS DIAMOND STICKPIN COLLECTION IN HIS DRESSING-ROOM! I'LL JUST TAKE THEM IF YOU DON'T MIND!

3

AN HOUR LATER, ABOARD THE YACHT, "SUPREME", DOCKED AT THE GOTHAM BOAT CLUB...

HOW FITTING MY NEXT CRIME SHOULD TAKE PLACE ABOARD A YACHT WITH A **TWIN-SCREW** PROPELLER ASSEMBLY! HA-HA!

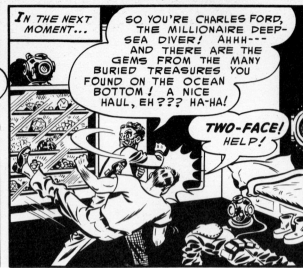

IN THE NEXT MOMENT...

SO YOU'RE CHARLES FORD, THE MILLIONAIRE DEEP-SEA DIVER! AHHH--- AND THERE ARE THE GEMS FROM THE MANY BURIED TREASURES YOU FOUND ON THE OCEAN BOTTOM! A NICE HAUL, EH??? HA-HA!

TWO-FACE! HELP!

NEXT DAY AT POLICE HEADQUARTERS, AS **BATMAN** AND **ROBIN** RESPOND TO AN URGENT SUMMONS SENT OUT BY COMMISSIONER GORDON...

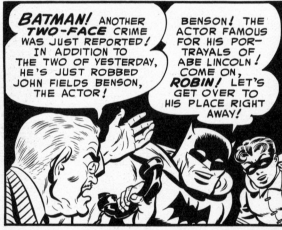

BATMAN! ANOTHER **TWO-FACE** CRIME WAS JUST REPORTED! IN ADDITION TO THE TWO OF YESTERDAY, HE'S JUST ROBBED JOHN FIELDS BENSON, THE ACTOR!

BENSON! THE ACTOR FAMOUS FOR HIS PORTRAYALS OF ABE LINCOLN! COME ON, **ROBIN!** LET'S GET OVER TO HIS PLACE RIGHT AWAY!

SOON AFTER, IN THE ACTOR'S APARTMENT...

I'D JUST COME HOME AFTER THE MATINEE PERFORMANCE-- I DON'T BOTHER TO REMOVE MY MAKE-UP BETWEEN THE MATINEE AND EVENING SHOW-- WHEN **TWO-FACE** BURST IN UPON ME!

AND HE STOLE YOUR VALUABLE COLLECTION OF LINCOLN'S PAPERS! HMMM--- THIS IS NOT LIKE THE **TWO-FACE** OF OLD!

LATER, IN THE SECRET **BATCAVE**, AS THE FAMED LAWMEN REVERT TO THEIR EVERY-DAY ROLES AS SOCIALITE BRUCE WAYNE AND HIS WARD, DICK GRAYSON...

TWO-FACE HAS COME BACK-- HOW, WHY, WE DON'T KNOW AS YET! BUT EVEN MORE PUZZLING ARE THE CRIMES HE'S COMMITTING! THERE'S NO PATTERN TO THEM!

MAYBE HE'S JUST MAD--- AND HE'S STRIKING WHEREVER HIS FANCY CARRIES HIM!

THEN...

NO, DICK! I'VE GOT IT! I'VE FOUND THE THREAD THAT BINDS THESE THREE CRIMES TOGETHER!

SNAP!

HOW ABOUT **YOU**??? ARE **YOU** AS CLEVER AS THE GREAT **BATMAN**? HAVE YOU CAUGHT ON TO **TWO-FACE'S** SCHEME?

④

ALL AT ONCE...

THIS IS THE QUICKEST WAY OUT OF HERE! GET SET FOR A TOBOGGAN SLIDE, ROBIN!

I'M RIGHT BEHIND YOU!

AND, AS THE DARING LAWMEN WHIZ DOWN THE RUNWAY THAT NORMALLY CARRIES THE BALL FROM A POCKET TO THE END-TRAY...

BATMAN I'M STUCK! MY FOOT'S CAUGHT!

GOLLY! ONE OF THOSE LOOSE BALLS IS ABOUT TO DROP INTO THIS POCKET! IT'LL COME ROARING DOWN THIS CHUTE LIKE AN EXPRESS TRAIN! I'VE GOT TO SAVE ROBIN!

BACK-TRACKING SWIFTLY, BATMAN MANIPULATES HIS SILKEN ROPE WITH LIGHTNING-LIKE RAPIDITY...

QUICK THINKING, BATMAN! THAT NET YOU MADE OUT OF YOUR SILKEN CORD HAS TRAPPED THE BALL AND SAVED MY LIFE!

NOW TO FREE YOU AS QUICKLY AS POSSIBLE!

LATER...

THEY'RE GONE! THEY TOOK ADVANTAGE OF OUR MISHAP UNDER THE POOL TABLE TO MAKE GOOD THEIR ESCAPE!

BUT AT LEAST YOU SCARED TWO-FACE OFF BEFORE HE COULD CARRY OUT HIS PLAN! HE WAS GOING TO CLEAN OUT EVERY CENT I HAD IN MY SAFE!

YOU KNOW, ROBIN, I THINK WE CAN SCRAP OUR LIST OF POSSIBLE TWO-FACE VICTIMS. IT APPEARS NOW THAT TWO-FACE ISN'T GOING TO BE AS OBVIOUS AS WE THOUGHT!

WHICH MEANS WE'LL HAVE TO BE MORE ALERT THAN EVER TO SPOT HIS NEXT MOVE!

NEXT MORNING, AS BRUCE AND DICK FINISH THEIR BREAKFAST IN THE WAYNE HOME...

DICK--- THAT HEADLINE! IT GIVES ME AN IDEA JUST WILD ENOUGH TO FIT INTO TWO-FACE'S CURRENT SCHEME!

WAIT-- I THINK I FOLLOW YOU! WHEN AN ORIENTAL IS DISGRACED, IT IS CLAIMED THAT HE "LOST FACE"! THAT WOULD GIVE THIS FELLOW TWO FACES --- HIS REAL ONE, AND THE ONE HE "LOST"! COME ON! LET'S CHECK IT!

The Gotham Gazette
JAPANESE ENVOY RECALLED; CITED FOR MISCONDUCT BY OWN GOVERNMENT

7

177

SOON AFTER, AS THE HAPLESS **BATMAN** AND **ROBIN** ARE STRAPPED WITH WIRE ACROSS THE "GOOD FACE" OF THE HUGE COIN...

THIS LOOKS LIKE A FIFTY-FIFTY CHANCE, **ROBIN**-- BUT IT ISN'T! OUR WEIGHT WILL SURELY TIP THE COIN SO THAT WE COME DOWN ON THE SPIKES-- AND **TWO-FACE** KNOWS IT!

HURRY AND FIX THAT MECHANISM! I CAN'T WAIT FOR THE TOSS OF **THIS** COIN!

MINUTES PASS, SLOWLY, AGONIZINGLY! AND THEN THE CATAPULT MECHANISM IS READY! AT A SIGNAL FROM **TWO-FACE**, THE COIN IS LAUNCHED INTO THE AIR!

HA-HA! WHAT AN IDEA THIS WAS! THE GREATEST OF MY CAREER!

UP SPINS THE COIN, TO THE TOP OF ITS ARC-- AND THEN DOWN IT STARTS, TURNING OVER AND OVER...

DOWN... DOWN... EVER SPINNING... GETTING CLOSER AND CLOSER!

AND THEN A SUDDEN CRAZY FLIP, AND THE COIN LANDS **GOOD SIDE UP!**

THEY LANDED SAFELY-- AND THEY'VE SNAPPED THEIR BONDS! EVERYTHING'S GONE WRONG! EVERYTHING! I DON'T UNDERSTAND!

HITTING LIKE TWIN BLASTS OF DYNAMITE, THE LAWMEN SAIL INTO THE DEMORALIZED CROOKS...

YOUR MEN BOUND US TOO TIGHTLY WITH THAT WIRE! BY STRAINING AGAINST IT JUST BEFORE WE LANDED, **ROBIN** AND I DREW IT TRIGGER-TAUT! THE SOLID, SHARP LANDING IMPACT SNAPPED IT!

BUT HOW DID YOU LAND GOOD SIDE UP? IT WAS PRACTICALLY AN IMPOSSIBILITY!

YOU SLIPPED UP! YOU STRAPPED US TO THAT COIN IN SUCH A WAY THAT OUR HANDS COULD REACH OUR BELT RADIOS! YOU NEVER NOTICED US FIDDLING WITH OUR RADIOS, CHANGING CONNECTIONS, TURNING THE RADIOS INTO **ELECTRO-MAGNETS!**

BY CONNECTING THESE MAGNETS WITH YOUR **WIRE BINDINGS**, WE SET UP A POWERFUL **NEGATIVE MAGNETIC FIELD!** IT **REPELLED** THOSE SPIKES-- MAKING THE COIN LAND THE WAY IT DID!

THE END

10

ON GOTHAM CITY RIVER, AN OVER-LOADED BARGE CARRYING HIGH EX-PLOSIVES, THREATENS A FREAK DISASTER...

THE BARGE IS SINKING! I'M GETTING OUT OF HERE!

ME TOO! THE NITRO-GLYCERINE WE'RE CARRYING MAY EXPLODE!

AND WHEN PERIL LOOMS, A FAMOUS SYMBOL SWEEPS THE SKY TO SUMMON BATMAN AND ROBIN -- SECRETLY BRUCE WAYNE AND HIS WARD, DICK GRAYSON...

THE BAT-SIGNAL, BRUCE! IT COULD BE ANOTHER OF THOSE PLATINUM ROBBERY-ATTEMPTS!

UNTIL WE CATCH "SLANT" STACEY AND HIS PLATINUM BANDITS, WE'LL GET NO REST! LET'S GET INTO COSTUME-- FAST!

BUT IT IS A GREATER EMERGENCY WHICH HAS SUMMONED THE CAPED MAN-HUNTERS TO COMMISSIONER GORDON'S OFFICE...

IF THE CANS OF NITRO ON THAT SUNKEN BARGE DRIFT AND EXPLODE, THEY'LL DESTROY HALF THE WATERFRONT! BUT NO DIVER WILL RISK GOING DOWN TO RETRIEVE THEM!

ROBIN AND I HAVE PRACTICED DEEP-SEA DIVING! GET US A PAIR OF DIVING SUITS, AND WE'LL GO DOWN!

SOON, ON A BARGE IN THE MIDDLE OF THE RIVER...

TIE THE NITRO CANS ONTO THE ROPE SLINGS WE LET DOWN, AND WE'LL DRAW THEM UP CAREFULLY! BUT REMEMBER--DON'T STAY DOWN TOO LONG IN THAT PRESSURE!

THE PHONE WORKS FINE--I HEAR YOU! LOWER AWAY!

FOR NEARLY AN HOUR, BATMAN AND ROBIN LABOR AWAY FAR BENEATH THE SURFACE...

HAUL THESE CANS UP! WE'VE ONLY A FEW MORE TO RETRIEVE!

BUT BATMAN.. YOU'RE STAYING DOWN IN THAT PRESSURE TOO LONG! COME UP-- AT ONCE!

NO-- WE MUST GET THESE LAST CANS, OR THEY'LL DRIFT AWAY AND DESTROY DOCKS AND BRIDGES!

BUT YOU'VE STAYED SO LONG DOWN THERE, YOU CAN'T COME UP NOW-- OR YOU'LL DIE FROM THE "BENDS!"

THE "BENDS"--TERRIBLE PHYSICAL COLLAPSE THAT STRIKES DIVERS WHO RISE TO THE SURFACE TOO RAPIDLY! DOES THIS DOOM THE DYNAMIC DUO?

2

YOU MUST STAY UNDERSEA FOR TWO DAYS NOW, AND REDUCE THE PRESSURE GRADUALLY BEFORE YOU COME UP!

IN THAT CASE, YOU'LL HAVE TO GET US SOME SORT OF SUBMARINE, EQUIPPED WITH PRESSURE CONTROLS!

A NEARBY SALVAGE COMPANY IS GLAD TO HELP OUT BATMAN...

SURE... BATMAN CAN BORROW THIS SURPLUS NAVY POCKET-SUB THAT WE USE FOR SALVAGE! I'LL FIX IT UP SPECIAL!

THANK YOU!

AND IT'S THE STRANGEST SUBMARINE IN HISTORY THAT SOON IS LOWERED TO BATMAN AND ROBIN...

WE CAN ENTER IT THROUGH THE SMALL AIR-LOCK ESCAPE HATCH!

THEY PAINTED THE BAT-EMBLEM ON IT! IT'S A REGULAR BATMARINE NOW!

SHORTLY, INSIDE...

WE'LL REDUCE THE AIR PRESSURE IN HERE SLOWLY, SO THAT IN A FEW DAYS, WE CAN EMERGE AGAIN!

WHAT'S BOTHERING ME, THOUGH, IS HOW'LL WE FIGHT CRIME FROM UNDERWATER? "SLANT" STACY'S PLATINUM BANDITS WILL BE ABLE TO RUN WILD NOW!

EXACTLY WHAT "SLANT" STACY, MASTERMIND OF A BANK SYNDICATE, THINKS TOO...

NOW WE CAN STRIKE AT ALL THE PLATINUM HOARDES WE DIDN'T DARE TRY BEFORE! THE ART JEWELRY COMPANY'S SHIPMENT IS FIRST ON OUR LIST!

BUT BATMAN'S CLEVER, BOSS! HE MAY STILL TRY TO STOP US!

ART JEWELRY CO.

DON'T WORRY... IF BATMAN INTERFERES WITH US NOW, I CAN STOP HIM FOR GOOD! DON'T FORGET, I'VE GOT A SETUP THAT NO CROOK EVER HAD BEFORE!

3

WHILE AT THE OTHER END OF THE LONG HALL...

I THOUGHT I SAW SOMEONE IN THAT BIG TANK OVER THERE!

YOU'RE NERVOUS ABOUT WATER NOW... BUT WE'LL LOOK OVER THE TANKS ANYHOW, TO MAKE SURE BATMAN ISN'T HERE!

KNOWING THAT DISCOVERY IS IMMINENT, BATMAN ACTS SWIFTLY...

AN OCTOPUS, WHEN ATTACKED, CLOUDS THE WATER BY EMITTING INK-- AND WE NEED COVER RIGHT NOW! THIS WILL ONLY SCARE HIM!

THUS, BY THE TIME THE CROOKS REACH THE TANK...

THAT'S ALL YOU SAW-- AN OCTOPUS! AND IT'S MORE SCARED THAN YOU ARE, THE WAY IT COVERED UP! COME ON-- LET'S GET THAT PLATINUM!

GOT TO ACT FAST, ROBIN, AND THERE'S ONLY ONE WAY... I'M GOING BACK TO OPEN THE MAIN VALVES WIDE!

AND MINUTES LATER, FURTIVE CRIMESTERS GET A STARTLING SURPRISE...

HEY! THE TANKS ARE OVERFLOWING! THERE'S SOMETHING WRONG HERE!

IT'S BATMAN, SOMEWHERE! HE'S FLOODING THE HALL SO HE CAN GET AT US! WE GOTTA SKIP OUT OF HERE, FAST!

AS THE ALARMED CROOKS FLEE, BATMAN CLOSES THE GIANT VALVES!

THE WATER WILL DRAIN AWAY WITHOUT HARMING THE MARBLE HALL! BUT WE DIDN'T GET A CHANCE TO GRAB THEM!

WELL-- AT LEAST WE BROKE UP THEIR PLANS... AND I'LL BET THEY'RE RAGING!

7

187

IT'S FURIOUS MOBSTERS INDEED WHO LATER CONFRONT THEIR LEADER...

YOU AND YOUR SCHEMES! EVEN WITHOUT BEING ABLE TO COME OUT OF WATER, *BATMAN'S* TOO MUCH FOR YOU!

YOU THINK SO? I TOLD YOU I HAD A WAY TO GET *BATMAN* IF HE PERSISTED... NOW LISTEN TO IT!

AND WHEN AN EVIL PLAN HAS BEEN UNFOLDED, TEMPERS CHANGE...

WHAT AN IDEA! IT'LL FIX *BATMAN* FOR SURE!

YEAH-- IF HE INTERFERES WITH US THIS TIME, NOTHING CAN SAVE HIM FROM DEATH!

WHAT IS STACY'S SINISTER SCHEME? IT STARTS ON THE POST OFFICE ROOF, WHERE A MAIL-HELICOPTER PILOT PREPARES TO TAKE OFF...

INSTEAD OF MAIL, YOU'RE DELIVERING *US* -- TO THE ROOF OF THE *GOTHAM SKYSCRAPER!* AND WHEN WE'RE THROUGH THERE, YOU'LL TAKE US AWAY AGAIN!

AND WHEN THEY REACH THEIR DESTINATION...

I'LL KEEP HIM COVERED HERE!

IT'LL TAKE US TIME TO BLAST OPEN THE *PLATINUM CORPORATION'S* BIG SAFE -- SO FIRST WE'LL MAKE SURE THE POLICE CAN'T INTERFERE!

A LITTLE LATER, INSIDE...

THERE! WITH THE ELEVATOR-CABLES SLASHED, AND A SECTION OF THE STAIR CUT OUT, NO ONE CAN GET UP AT US -- EXCEPT MAYBE THE *BATMAN!*

AND IF *HE* LEAVES THE WATER TO COME UP HERE, HE'LL DIE OF THE "BENDS"!

AND IRONICALLY, TO THE *BATMARINE* COMES THE FIRST ALARM...

NO, *ROBIN*, THIS ISN'T A PRESSURE-SUIT! IT'S SOMETHING I'VE BUILT IN CASE WE NEED IT! THE WAY IT WORKS IS...

WAIT, *BATMAN!* THROUGH THE PERISCOPE, I CAN SEE THE *BAT-SIGNAL!*

8

THEY'RE FLASHING A MESSAGE IN POLICE CODE! BANDITS BLASTING PLATINUM CORPORATION SAFE. STAIRS AND ELEVATORS BLOCKED!

STACY FIGURES WE CAN'T GET UP THERE TO STOP HIM! BUT I *MUST* ANSWER THAT CALL!

BATMAN, NO!! IF YOU LEAVE THIS SUB, IT'S DEATH FOR YOU! YOU KNOW THAT!

YES, YES -- I KNOW... I HAVE NO CHOICE!

SO MOMENTS LATER, FROM THE TORPEDO-TUBE OF THE *BATMARINE* HURTLES A GRIM FIGURE...

AND A CITY SEES ITS GREATEST HERO EMERGE TO CERTAIN DOOM...

IT'S *BATMAN*, HEADING FOR THE *GOTHAM SKYSCRAPER!*

HE'LL DIE OF THE "BENDS" FOR SURE! WHY DID HE SACRIFICE HIS LIFE LIKE THIS?

HE'S CLIMBING TO THE ROOF-- THE ONLY MAN WHO COULD REACH IT BEFORE THEY ESCAPED IN THAT COMMANDEERED HELICOPTER!

BUT HE CAN'T LAST LONG... THE "BENDS" WILL KILL HIM ANY MINUTE!

BATMAN! HE CAME UP OUTSIDE THE BUILDING!

HE'S DOOMED! HE CAN'T LIVE FOR LONG NOW!

BUT THE GRIM CAPED FIGURE HAS ENOUGH LIFE TO FINISH HIS TASK...

GREAT WORK, *BATMAN!* I'LL BRING THE POLICE HERE FAST IN MY 'COPTER!

MAYBE YOU CAUGHT US, *BATMAN* -- BUT *WE* GOT *YOU*, TOO! THIS FEAT WILL COST YOU YOUR LIFE!

9

ONE NIGHT, AS THE FAMED **BAT-PLANE** SOARS OVER MOUNTAINOUS TERRAIN, FAR FROM **GOTHAM CITY**...

IN ABOUT TEN HOURS, WE'LL BE BACK HOME! I CAN'T SAY I WON'T BE GLAD!

SAME HERE! THESE DISTANT MISSIONS MAKE ME HOMESICK!

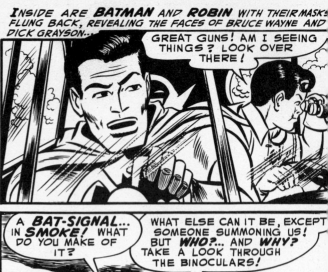

INSIDE ARE **BATMAN** AND **ROBIN** WITH THEIR MASKS FLUNG BACK, REVEALING THE FACES OF BRUCE WAYNE AND DICK GRAYSON...

GREAT GUNS! AM I SEEING THINGS? LOOK OVER THERE!

A **BAT-SIGNAL**... IN **SMOKE!** WHAT DO YOU MAKE OF IT?

WHAT ELSE CAN IT BE, EXCEPT SOMEONE SUMMONING US! BUT **WHO?**... AND **WHY?** TAKE A LOOK THROUGH THE BINOCULARS!

THIS GETS MORE INCREDIBLE BY THE MINUTE! THERE'S A BOY DOWN THERE WHO LOOKS EXACTLY LIKE **ME!**

STUNNED BY THESE SURPRISING EVENTS, THE CAPED CRIME-FIGHTERS HURRIEDLY LAND THE **BAT-PLANE** IN A SHELTERED CLEARING, AND...

A **BATSIGNAL** IN THE FORM OF SMOKE-- A BOY WHO LOOKS EXACTLY LIKE YOU, **ROBIN**... THIS CALLS FOR AN IMMEDIATE INVESTIGATION! COME ON!

AND DEEP IN THE WOODS, STILL ANOTHER SURPRISE...A CANOE BEARING A **BAT-SYMBOL**, AND A CAVERN NOT UNLIKE THEIR OWN **BAT-CAVE!**

BUT WHAT CAN THIS MEAN?

LISTEN... VOICES INSIDE THE CAVE LET'S HAVE A LOOK

A MOMENT LATER, INSIDE...

NO, FATHER! YOU CAN'T GO OUT NOW AS CHIEF MAN-OF-THE-BATS! YOUR WOUND WILL BETRAY YOU!

BATMAN! ROBIN! THE GREAT MYSTERY HAS SENT YOU!

WHAT...?

CHIEF MAN-OF-THE-BATS? I DON'T UNDER-STAND!

GREAT EAGLE IS MY REAL NAME, O BATMAN--AND THIS IS MY SON, LITTLE RAVEN! WE ARE OF THE SIOUX TRIBE! LONG HAVE WE PLAYED THE ROLES OF BATMAN AND ROBIN!

WHEN DRESSED AS YOU, I AM KNOWN AS CHIEF MAN-OF-THE-BATS! IN OUR WAR AGAINST CRIME, WE OPERATE HERE, FROM OUR OWN VERSION OF A BAT-CAVE!

AMAZING! BUT TELL ME-- HOW WERE YOU WOUNDED?

VILLAINOUS BLACK ELK AND HIS RAIDERS HAVE BEEN TERRORIZING THE COUNTRYSIDE, AND WE HAVE BEEN TRYING TO PUT AN END TO THEM! BUT JUST TODAY...

"...BLACK ELK LED A RAID ON MY VILLAGE AND BEFORE I COULD SWITCH TO MAN-OF-THE-BATS, HIS SPEAR THRUST FOUND MY SHOULDER!"

HA, GREAT EAGLE! YOU CANNOT STAND BEFORE ME!

LONG HAVE I THOUGHT YOU AND MAN-OF-THE-BATS TO BE THE SAME PERSON! WELL, NOW WE SHALL SEE! IF MAN-OF-THE-BATS APPEARS WITH A WOUNDED SHOULDER, I SHALL THEN KNOW HIS TRUE IDENTITY!

3

HMM... WE'VE RUN INTO SIMILAR PROBLEMS, TRYING TO PROTECT *OUR* REAL IDENTITIES! BUT *LITTLE RAVEN* IS RIGHT... YOU CAN'T APPEAR AS *MAN-OF-THE-BATS* WITH THAT WOUNDED SHOULDER!

THEN WHAT CAN BE DONE? IF HE *DOESN'T* APPEAR, ALL SHALL KNOW IT IS BECAUSE OF THE SPEAR WOUND... AND ALL SHALL KNOW MY TRUE IDENTITY!

ARE YOU THINKING THE SAME THING I AM, *ROBIN?*

I'D SAY SO!

GREAT EAGLE, SUPPOSING *ROBIN* AND I PLAYED THE ROLES OF *CHIEF MAN OF-THE-BATS* AND *LITTLE RAVEN?*

THAT WOULD INDEED SAVE THE SITUATION! HERE... WE MUST GET YOU INTO MY COSTUME -- AND ACQUAINT YOU WITH MY UTILITY BELT!

THE BELT CONTAINS DYES--WHICH YOU CAN APPLY TO YOUR SKINS!

THUS, WITHIN A FEW SHORT MINUTES...

THERE! THE DISGUISE IS COMPLETE! NONE COULD GUESS YOU ARE NOT ME! BUT YOU MUST TAKE ONE PRECAUTION...

YOU MUST PERFORM *ONLY* IN INDIAN FASHION! IF NOT, PEOPLE WILL GUESS IMMEDIATELY THAT YOU ARE STAND-INS FOR US!

WELL, OUR JOB'S CUT OUT FOR US! LET'S HEAD FOR OUR FIRST ENCOUNTER WITH *BLACK ELK'S* RAIDERS!

4

MEANWHILE, AT A SPRAWLING OIL FIELD NOT FAR AWAY...

THE ARMORED CAR WITH THE PAYROLL APPROACHES! QUICKLY--TO YOUR STATIONS!

A BOW TWANGS, THEN ANOTHER--AND ANOTHER...

POOF!

FFT! SSSSSS!

SWERVING, THE CAR SMASHES INTO THE BASE OF THE DERRICK...

THEY'LL NEVER CRACK THROUGH OUR ARMOR! LET 'EM HAVE IT!

CRASH!

BUT BEFORE THE GUARDS CAN OPEN FIRE, FLAMING SHAFTS STREAK THROUGH THE GUN SLOTS...

YOW! ARROWS SATURATED WITH KEROSENE! THEY'RE SETTING THE CAR ON FIRE!

RUSHING OUT FRANTICALLY, THE GUARDS ARE QUICKLY SUBDUED...

NOW--THE PAYROLL! MAKE HASTE-- BEFORE THE FLAMES CONSUME IT!

BUT, AT THAT MOMENT, ATTRACTED BY THE BLAZE BELOW, TWO FIGURES SWING FROM ONE OF THE TOWERING DERRICKS...

HERE WE GO! OUR FIRST TEST AS INDIANS!

MAN-OF-THE-BATS! SLAY HIM!

5

AND AS THE RAIDERS GALLOP OFF...
THEY'RE GETTING AWAY-- BUT PUTTING THAT FIRE OUT IS MORE IMPORTANT RIGHT NOW! IF THE FLAMES EVER REACH THE STORAGE TANKS-- AS **BLACK ELK** SAID-- **EVERYTHING** WILL GO UP!

A TWO-MAN **BUCKET BRIGADE** OUGHT TO TURN THE TRICK!

SHORTLY...
INJUNS-- YOU SAVED THE PAYROLL! THANKS!

WE HAVE OTHER WORK NOW! WE ARE GOING AFTER **BLACK ELK!**

LATER, AS THEY SCAN THE NEARBY TERRAIN...
COME ON... WE'LL GET THE **BATPLANE** AND FOLLOW THEM!

NO! WE'VE GOT TO HANDLE THIS LIKE **INDIANS**--REMEMBER! HERE'S THEIR TRAIL-- HEADING SOUTH TOWARD THE RIVER!

AND AT THE RIVER, WHERE, AT FIRST, THE TRAIL SEEMS LOST FOREVER...
SEE BELOW, ON THE RIVER'S BOTTOM? SMALL STONES AND PEBBLES HAVE BEEN OVERTURNED! THAT PATTERN CONTINUES SOUTHWARD!

THE STONES WERE DISTURBED BY HORSES' FEET! EVEN THOUGH THE ACTUAL TRACKS ARE WASHED AWAY-- WE NOW KNOW WHICH DIRECTION **BLACK ELK** TOOK!

THEY'LL HAVE TO LEAVE THE RIVER SOMETIME... AND WHEN THEY DO, WE'LL BE ABLE TO PICK UP THEIR TRAIL AGAIN!

BUT SOME MILES FURTHER ON, THE TRACKS EMERGE FROM THE RIVER ONLY TO END ABRUPTLY, AT THE EDGE OF A VAST, STONY FLATNESS...
THEY HEADED ACROSS THE LAVA FLATS! HORSES DON'T LEAVE PRINTS IN HARD STONE! WE'RE BEATEN!

NO! NOT YET! AGAIN WE'VE GOT TO PLAY INDIAN! **GREAT EAGLE** WOULD FIND THE TRAIL... SO WILL WE!

INDIAN PONIES DON'T WEAR HORSESHOES... BUT SEE THESE SMALL SCRAPINGS OF BONY SUBSTANCE? THAT WAS LEFT BY THE **FEET** OF THEIR HORSES!

THEN WE CAN **STILL** FOLLOW THEM! **GREAT EAGLE** SHOULD BE PROUD OF US FOR FIGURING THIS ONE OUT!

7

ALL RIGHT-- LET'S GO!

WE'RE SAFE FOR NOW--BUT THEY THINK THEY HAVE THE PLACE SURROUNDED! CAPTURE MEANS THE STRIPPING OFF OF OUR MASKS!

I KNOW! BUT THEY THINK WE'RE REALLY *GREAT EAGLE* AND *LITTLE RAVEN*... AND WE HAVE ONE TRICK LEFT!

SWIFTLY, BATMAN REMOVES SOME TINY MISSILES FROM THE UTILITY BELT, AND...

SMOKE PELLETS! THAT'S OUR OUT!

AS THE PELLETS STRIKE THE FLOOR AND BURST, THICK CLOUDS BILLOW SKYWARD...

NOW, SOMEHOW, WE'VE GOT TO STALL THE RAIDERS! GET YOUR BOW AND ARROWS READY!

WE'VE GOT YOU, *GREAT EAGLE!* I KNOW THAT YOU AND *MAN-OF-THE-BATS* ARE ONE AND THE SAME!

ONLY ONE ARROW LEFT! AFTER THAT, IT'S CURTAINS! WE'VE PROTECTED *GREAT EAGLE'S* IDENTITY--BUT NOW WE'RE IN DANGER OF REVEALING OUR OWN!

LISTEN! THEY'RE SHOUTING ABOUT SOMETHING!

LOOK, O *BLACK ELK!* IT IS *GREAT EAGLE* HIMSELF! HE AND *MAN-OF-THE-BATS* CANNOT POSSIBLY BE THE SAME PERSON!

THEN WHO *CAN MAN-OF-THE-BATS* BE?

9

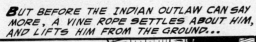

BUT BEFORE THE INDIAN OUTLAW CAN SAY MORE, A VINE ROPE SETTLES ABOUT HIM, AND LIFTS HIM FROM THE GROUND...

A QUESTION YOU SHALL NEVER ANSWER, *BLACK ELK!*

DON'T LET ME FALL...

THEN TELL YOUR RAIDERS TO LAY DOWN THEIR ARMS, AND SUBMIT TO *GREAT EAGLE!* AND TALK FAST, MY HANDS GROW TIRED!

AND SO, PRESENTLY...

MANY JAILS ARE ANXIOUS TO ACCOMODATE *BLACK ELK!* THANKS TO YOU, *MAN-OF-THE-BATS*, HE AND HIS RAIDERS SOON WILL BE BEHIND BARS!

I WONDER WHO YOU ARE, *MAN-OF-THE-BATS!* SOME DAY, I SHALL FIND OUT!

MUCH LATER, BACK AT GREAT EAGLE'S CAVE...

YOUR REAL IDENTITY REMAINS A SECRET... BUT NOW WE MUST LEAVE! THE *BAT-PLANE* IS NEARBY, AND WE HAVE MANY MILES TO COVER TONIGHT!

HAD I NOT SEEN YOUR SMOKE SIGNALS, *BLACK ELK* MAY HAVE LEARNED OF *YOUR* IDENTITY! BUT THAT, TOO, REMAINS A SECRET! FARE-WELL, *BATMAN!*

AND AS THE BAT-PLANE TAKES OFF FOR GOTHAM CITY...

WHO KNOW?... MAYBE ONE DAY, MY SON, *WE* CAN GO TO THE GREAT CITY AND DO *THEM* A FAVOR! WE SHALL SEE!

THE END

10

200

A PUZZLING PROBLEM, INDEED, AS THE BOY WONDER JOINS **BATMAN** AT THE PAPER MILL...

YOU SAY ONLY ONE BALE OF THAT PAR-TICULAR PAPER WAS STOLEN?

YES, THAT'S ALL! I CAN'T UNDERSTAND IT-- THE PAPER'S NOT THAT VALUABLE -- AND... WH--WHAT'S THAT?

GR-R

WHY, **BAT-HOUND...** WHAT'S THE MATTER WITH YOU?

I WAS RIGHT ABOUT THIS PAPER ROBBERY! **BAT-HOUND** PROVES IT!

GRRRR GRRRR

BAT-HOUND HAS SCENTED THE BURGLARS' TRAIL HERE! BUT WHY SHOULD THAT ENRAGE HIM SO, UNLESS...

UNLESS THEY'RE THE SAME MEN WHO STUNNED HIM AND ABDUCTED HIS MASTER, JOHN WILKER! AND IF MY THEORY IS RIGHT, THEY'LL STRIKE NEXT AT THE 'BIG **EASTERN PRINTING-INK COMPANY!**

MOMENTS LATER...

BUT WHY SHOULD CROOKS WANT PAPER AND INK? I DON'T GET IT!

IT WAS **SPECIAL** PAPER THEY STOLE, **ROBIN** -- THE KIND VALUABLE **BONDS** ARE PRINTED ON! WITH WILKER TO ENGRAVE AND PRINT FOR THEM, AND THE RIGHT PAPER AND INK, THEY CAN **COUNTERFEIT BONDS!**

AND WHEN THEY REACH THE INK FACTORY...

BAT-HOUND! COME BACK! HE'S GONE WILD, FOR SOME REASON...

EASTERN PRINTIN

ARF! ARF! ARF!

BAT-HOUND HAS A VERY **GOOD** REASON...

THAT MASKED DOG... IT'S MY OWN DOG-- ACE!

THAT MUTT AGAIN? THIS CAN OF INK WILL KNOCK HIM COLD!

WHERE IS BATWOMAN'S HIDEOUT, INDEED? AT THAT MOMENT...

THIS FORGOTTEN OLD MINE-TUNNEL IN THE SUBURBS CAME IN HANDY--

--FOR WHEN I BUILT MY HOUSE OVER THE TUNNEL, IT GAVE ME A HIDDEN BAT-CAVE UNDERNEATH! AND MY OWN PORTRAIT GUARDS MY BAT-CAVE FOR ME!

BATWOMAN

A CHANGE OF COSTUME, AND...

KATHY KANE, HEIRESS -- NO ONE WILL EVER DREAM I'M BATWOMAN -- OR HOW I CAME TO BE BATWOMAN!

"BECAUSE NO ONE DREAMS I WAS ONCE A CIRCUS DAREDEVIL PERFORMER!"

SHE'S A FINE TRAPEZE PERFORMER -- AND OUR BEST MOTOR-CYCLE STUNT RIDER TOO!

BUT I WISH I COULD BE LIKE BATMAN, THE GREATEST ACROBAT OF ALL! HE USES HIS SKILL, NOT FOR SHOWS, BUT AGAINST CRIME!

"BUT ONE DAY AN INHERITANCE GAVE ME A CHANCE TO REALIZE MY AMBITION!"

I INHERIT MY UNCLE'S ENTIRE FORTUNE! NOW I CAN USE MY SKILLS AS BATMAN DOES! I, TOO, WILL FIGHT CRIME -- I'LL BE A BATWOMAN!

"AND IN THIS BAT-CAVE I FITTED UP UNDER MY NEW MANSION, I TRAINED LONG FOR MY CAREER!"

THIS COSTUME WILL MASK MY IDENTITY! MY BAT-CYCLE IS READY, AND THIS SHOULDER-BAG UTILITY-CASE WILL BE A GREAT HELP. NOW, WITH MY CRIME-LABORATORY, MY FILES, EVERYTHING -- I'M READY TO ACT!

216

RETURNING TO THE UNCONSCIOUS **BATMAN**...

© 1956 National Comics Publications, Inc.

WEALTHY, LOVELY, YOUNG KATHY KANE SHOULD BE HAPPY, BUT...

SOMETIMES I ALMOST WISH I HADN'T INHERITED MY UNCLE'S FORTUNE! I'M SO BORED WITH JUST BEING A SOCIETY GIRL!

NOSTALGICALLY, KATHY DESCENDS TO A SECRET CAVERN BELOW HER MANSION...

-SIGH- LIFE WAS MORE EXCITING WHEN I WORE THIS COSTUME AS THE BATWOMAN!

BUT BATMAN FOUND OUT MY SECRET IDENTITY AND MADE ME REALIZE CROOKS COULD DO SO, TOO, EVENTUALLY-- AND ONCE THEY DID, I'D BE IN DANGER! SO I PROMISED TO GIVE UP MY BAT-WOMAN CAREER...

(BATMAN)

IF ONLY I COULD WEAR THIS COSTUME AGAIN, JUST ONCE! HMM... MAYBE I CAN-- AND WITH-OUT BREAKING MY PROMISE TO BATMAN! I CAN WEAR IT TO THE MASQUERADE BALL TONIGHT!

SO THAT NIGHT, IMPULSIVE KATHY EXCITEDLY SETS OUT...

I HOPE BRUCE WAYNE WILL BE AT THE PARTY! HE'S SO GOOD-LOOKING! I WONDER WHAT KIND OF COSTUME HE'LL WEAR?

LATER, ELSEWHERE, THE MYSTERIOUS BANDIT LEADER SNAPS HIS ORDERS...

WHEN THE TRAIN ENTERS THIS TUNNEL, WE'LL DERAIL IT AND GRAB THE VALUABLE PAINTINGS FROM THE MAIL CAR!

GEE, BOSS, YOU'RE ACTUALLY GONNA STAY WITH US ON A JOB FOR ONCE!

AT THAT MOMENT, BRUCE DONS A COSTUME -- NOT FOR A PARTY -- BUT FOR HIS CRIME-FIGHTING ROLE OF... BATMAN!

LET'S GO, DICK! I'VE GOT A LEAD TO THAT GANG THAT SPECIALIZES IN STEALING ART TREASURES!

I WONDER WHO THEIR BOSS IS, BRUCE? I HEAR HE'S ALWAYS MASKED-- THAT NOT EVEN HIS OWN GANG HAS EVER SEEN HIS FACE!

2

JUST THIS ONCE! I'VE GIVEN YOU A LIST OF OTHER JOBS TO DO BY YOUR-SELVES! CARRY THEM OUT AND I'LL CONTACT YOU LATER ON... HUH? *BATMAN AND ROBIN!*

AS THE CRIME-FIGHTERS TANGLE WITH THE GANG, THE TRAIN ROARS BY AND...

ROBIN, I'M GOING AFTER THEIR BOSS!

INTENT ON ESCAPE, THE CRIMINAL DOES NOT SEE BATMAN'S FOOT TWIST ON A PEBBLE...

UH-HHH! MY *ANKLE!*

AS THE TRAIN EMERGES FROM THE TUNNEL, A THICK PUFF OF ENGINE SMOKE BLOWS INTO THE BANDIT CHIEF'S FACE, AND...

THAT SMOKE--BLINDING ME-- CAN'T SEE-- YA-A-AA... I'M FALLING--FALLING!

THOUGH DAZED BY HIS FALL, HE INSTINCTIVELY RIDS HIMSELF OF THE ONE THING THAT WILL IDENTIFY HIM AS THE GANG LEADER...

GOT TO HIDE COWL-- BEFORE I PASS OUT...

A MOMENT LATER, AS FATE WOULD HAVE IT, KATHY DRIVES ONTO THE SCENE...

WHY...THERE'S *ROBIN*.. RUNNING TO THAT INJURED MAN! MAYBE HE NEEDS SOME HELP...

3

ROBIN-- LOOK! BATMAN'S HELPLESS-- AND THAT HUGE IDOL IS TOPPLING OVER ON HIM!

WITH SPLIT-SECOND PRECISION, TWO CAPED FIGURES LAUNCH FORWARD, SLAMMING THE BOGUS "BATMAN" TO SAFETY...

CRASH!

BY THE TIME THEY STAND ERECT AGAIN, THE BANDITS ARE GONE... EMPTY-HANDED...

HE ONLY HAD A FEW LESSONS-- SO HE WASN'T SURE OF HIMSELF, YET! THAT'S WHY HE HESITATED BEFORE!

NO... ACTUALLY, BRIGGS HESITATED BECAUSE, IN SPITE OF HIS AMNESIA, HE SENSED HE WAS WORKING AGAINST HIMSELF!

NEXT EVENING, BACK IN BATWOMAN'S CAVE, ROBIN DECIDES ON SOME STRATEGY...

PERHAPS IF I STREW AROUND SOME MAGAZINES AND NEWSPAPERS CONTAINING ART NEWS, BRIGGS WILL UNKNOWINGLY TIP US TO HIS GANG'S NEXT JOB... AS HE DID THE LAST TIME!

AND THE TRICK WORKS AS, SHORTLY AFTERWARD... HE'S FASCINATED BY THAT ART NOTICE... IT MUST BE THE NEXT JOB ON THAT LIST OF ROBBERIES HE PLANNED WITH HIS GANG!

BUT ROBIN IS UNAWARE THAT THE ART NOTICE HAS SUDDENLY JOLTED BRIGGS' MEMORY BACK TO NORMAL... NOW I REMEMBER! THE FALL FROM THE TRAIN... BATWOMAN'S LESSONS... EVERYTHING!

WOW-- WHAT A SETUP! BATMAN AND ROBIN MUST HAVE SOME PRIVATE REASON FOR STRINGING BATWOMAN ALONG THIS WAY... SO I'LL PRETEND I'VE STILL GOT AMNESIA-- AND LEAD HER AND THE KID RIGHT INTO A TRAP!

JADE BUDDHA

CHINATOWN MUSEUM

7

227

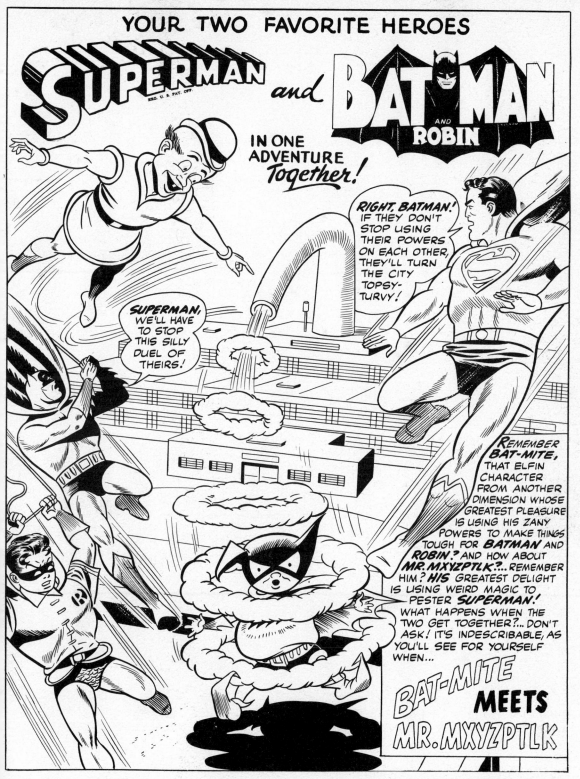

AT THIS VERY MOMENT, HOWEVER, NOT FAR AWAY...

BATMAN AND ROBIN DON'T KNOW I WAS SENT TO GOTHAM CITY AS CLARK KENT, TODAY, ON A STORY ASSIGNMENT! I CAN TAKE CARE OF THAT FLYING ROBOT FROM HERE!

I'LL TEAR THIS ROCK FREE AND HURL IT HARD ENOUGH TO SMASH THAT THING TO SMITHER-EENS!

RRRIP

NEXT INSTANT...

SOMEONE HURLED A GIANT BOULDER AT IT! THAT MUST BE...

SUPERMAN! HE'S HERE -- IN GOTHAM CITY! WHAT A BREAK!

BUT SUDDENLY...

TH-THE ROCK!... IT'S CHANGING INTO A COMIC FIGURE--OF SUPERMAN!

AND AS THE WEIRD FORM GOES PLUMMETING TO EARTH...

IT FELL RIGHT ACROSS THE STREET...BLOCKING TRAFFIC!

THIS INCREDIBLE INCIDENT CAN MEAN ONLY ONE THING...

OUR PESKY "PAL" FROM ANOTHER DIMENSION!

Y-YOU MEAN... BAT-MITE?

HE SURE DOES! GREETINGS, BATMAN AND ROBIN!

POP

3

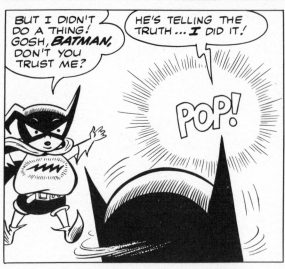

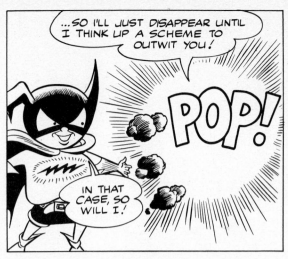

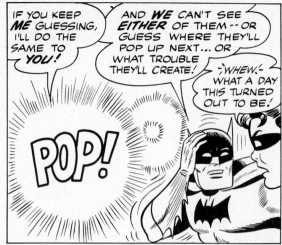

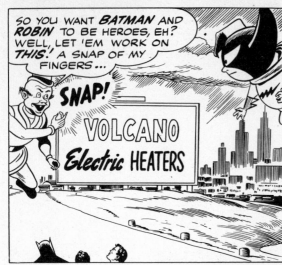

I, ALFRED, CONFIDENTIAL BUTLER TO BRUCE WAYNE, WHO IS SECRETLY BATMAN, AM RECORDING THE HISTORY FOLLOWING THE SADDEST EVENT IN MY LIFE...

"LAST WEEK, MY MASTER STUNNED THE WORLD WITH A DRAMATIC ANNOUNCEMENT..."

I AM AN OLD MAN NOW... IT IS TIME I RETIRED! AND SINCE ROBIN IS NOW A GROWN MAN, IT IS FITTING THAT HE SHOULD INHERIT MY MANTLE AND BECOME·BATMAN II!

"LATER, IN THE SECRET BAT-CAVE BENEATH OUR HOME, I WATCHED DICK GRAYSON, AS THE MASTER HUNG UP HIS BELOVED COSTUME FOREVER..."

WELL, DICK--YOU'RE BATMAN NOW! FROM NOW ON, YOU'LL BE FIGHTING CRIME ALL ALONE... YOU WON'T HAVE A ROBIN TO HELP YOU, AS YOU HELPED ME!

SURE HE DOES!... HE'S GOT ME!

"THE VOICE CAME FROM BRUCE WAYNE, JR.-- SON OF BATMAN AND KATHY KANE (BATWOMAN) WHOM HE HAD LONG AGO MARRIED..."

UNCLE DICK HAS BEEN TRAINING ME IN SECRET! GOSH, DAD, I WANT TO BE A CRIME-FIGHTER, JUST LIKE YOU AND MOM WERE!

NOW LOOK, YOUNGSTER-- I GAVE YOU SOME BASIC TRAINING, BUT I HAD NO IDEA YOU WANTED TO USE IT TO BECOME ANOTHER ROBIN!

PLEASE, DAD? I'M AS OLD AS UNCLE DICK WAS WHEN HE BECAME ROBIN! BESIDES, CRIME-FIGHTING RUNS IN THE FAMILY... I'M THE SON OF BATMAN AND BATWOMAN!

NO, BRUCE-- IT'S TOO DANGEROUS! I WON'T ALLOW IT!

"BRUCE, JR. EVENTUALLY WON HIS PARENTS OVER--AND BEGAN HIS TRAINING IN EARNEST..."

NOW THAT I'VE LEARNED JUDO, YOU'D BETTER NOT TRY SPANKING ME, DAD!

HA, HA!

2

"BECAUSE YOUNG BRUCE LEFT HURRIEDLY IN HIS *ROBIN* COSTUME, I THOUGHT IT BEST TO NOTIFY THE MASTER ..."

WHAT?... HE LEFT *ALONE?* I'D BETTER SEE WHAT HE WAS EXAMINING UNDER THE MICROSCOPE!

"ONE LOOK EXPLAINED EVERY-THING--AND THE MASTER CAME TO A QUICK DECISION..."

TATE COULD BE HIDING BABYFACE JORDAN! IF SO, HIS ENTIRE MOB WILL BE MEETING THERE! OUR BOY ISN'T EXPERIENCED ENOUGH TO HELP DICK HANDLE THAT GANG... IT COULD PROVE DANGEROUS ... THEY'LL NEED HELP!

YOU'RE NOT GOING WITHOUT *ME!* IF BRUCE, JR. IS IN DANGER, I WANT TO HELP, TOO! AFTER ALL, HE'S MY SON TOO!

NOW LOOK, HONEY-- YOU JUST CAN'T COME ALONG, AND THAT'S FINAL!

"NATURALLY, NO MAN EVER WINS AN ARGUMENT WITH A WOMAN--AND SO..."

NOT BAD FOR AN OLD GAL, EH? MY COSTUME STILL FITS ME-- THOUGH I DID HAVE TO COVER MY GRAYING HAIR WITH A WIG!

"MEANWHILE, *ROBIN II* HAD REACHED THE ENTRANCE TO THE OLD MICA QUARRY, AND CREPT STEALTHILY FORWARD..."

WE REALLY TOOK *BATMAN II* BY SURPRISE WHEN WE JUMPED HIM! WE'LL JUST KEEP HIM IN THE SHACK UNTIL BABYFACE DECIDES WHAT TO DO WITH HIM!

UNCLE DICK--CAPTURED! I'VE GOT TO FREE HIM ... BUT HOW CAN I GET PAST THOSE GUARDS? HMM--IF I CAN GET INTO THE ENGINE AND PUT ON THE HEADLIGHT...

6

"MOMENTS LATER, AS THE HEADLIGHT'S BEAM GLINTED GLARINGLY OFF THE LAYERS OF MICA CRYSTAL..."

AGGH! MY EYES!

THAT LIGHT-- I CAN'T SEE!

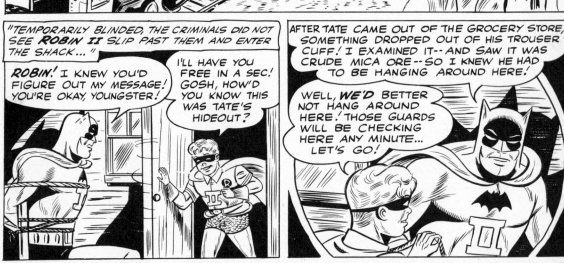

"TEMPORARILY BLINDED, THE CRIMINALS DID NOT SEE *ROBIN II* SLIP PAST THEM AND ENTER THE SHACK..."

ROBIN! I KNEW YOU'D FIGURE OUT MY MESSAGE! YOU'RE OKAY, YOUNGSTER!

I'LL HAVE YOU FREE IN A SEC! GOSH, HOW'D YOU KNOW THIS WAS TATE'S HIDEOUT?

AFTER TATE CAME OUT OF THE GROCERY STORE, SOMETHING DROPPED OUT OF HIS TROUSER CUFF! I EXAMINED IT-- AND SAW IT WAS CRUDE MICA ORE--SO I KNEW HE HAD TO BE HANGING AROUND HERE!

WELL, *WE'D* BETTER NOT HANG AROUND HERE! THOSE GUARDS WILL BE CHECKING HERE ANY MINUTE... LET'S GO!

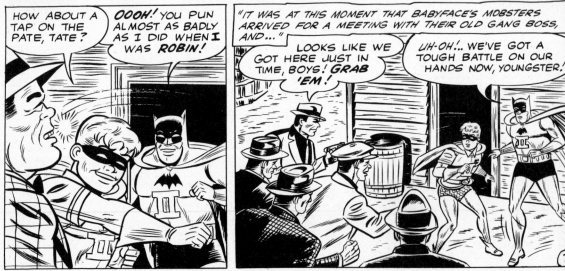

HOW ABOUT A TAP ON THE PATE, TATE?

OOOH! YOU PUN ALMOST AS BADLY AS I DID WHEN *I* WAS *ROBIN!*

"IT WAS AT THIS MOMENT THAT BABYFACE'S MOBSTERS ARRIVED FOR A MEETING WITH THEIR OLD GANG BOSS, AND..."

LOOKS LIKE WE GOT HERE JUST IN TIME, BOYS! *GRAB 'EM!*

UH-OH!... WE'VE GOT A TOUGH BATTLE ON OUR HANDS NOW, YOUNGSTER!

7

"WHAT A SPECTACLE!...THREE GENERATIONS OF CRIME-FIGHTERS, COMBINING FORCES TO COMBAT THE ENEMIES OF LAW AND ORDER!"

GOLLY--WE'RE LIKE THE *THREE MUSKETEERS!*

BUT WE DON'T NEED ANY SWORDS!

OUR FISTS ARE ALL WE NEED!

"LATER, WITH THE MOBSTERS IMPRISONED, THERE WAS A JOYOUS REUNION IN THE *BAT-CAVE*..."

YOU WERE WONDERFUL, SON... I'M PROUD OF YOU!

YES--IT LOOKS LIKE THE NEW TEAM OF *BATMAN* AND *ROBIN* IS HERE TO STAY!

ALFRED, WHAT ARE YOU UP TO?

HUH? OH...

WELL, YOU SEE, SIR--I JUST WANTED TO TRY OUT THIS NEW TYPEWRITER, AND BEFORE I REALIZED IT, I WAS *WRITING A STORY OF WHAT POSSIBLY MIGHT HAPPEN TO US ALL IN THE FUTURE!*

TOO BAD IT CAN'T BE PUBLISHED BECAUSE IT WOULD GIVE AWAY MY SECRET IDENTITY! NOBODY WILL EVER READ IT!

TRUE--NOBODY WILL EVER READ IT...BUT I HAD SO MUCH FUN WRITING THIS IMAGINARY STORY OF THE FUTURE THAT I THINK I'LL WRITE ANOTHER ONE SOMETIME ...

The End

Later, as **BATWOMAN,** puzzled by the girl's identity, returns to her lair...

WELL--DID I DO ALL RIGHT, AUNT KATHY?

BETTY! SO IT'S YOU! AND YOU'VE LEARNED MY SECRET DISGUISE!

WHO IS THIS AMAZING TEEN-AGER? HOW AND WHY DID SHE ASSUME THIS DISGUISE? FOR THE ANSWERS, WE MUST GLANCE BACK TO SOME DAYS BEFORE...

...WHEN WEALTHY HEIRESS, KATHY KANE, HAD AN UNEXPECTED VISITOR...

HI, AUNT KATHY! YOU ONCE SAID I COULD VISIT YOU -- SO HERE I AM!

THIS WILL COMPLICATE THINGS! I'LL BE SECRETLY GOING OUT SO MUCH AS **BATWOMAN,** I HOPE IT DOESN'T AROUSE HER SUSPICION!

As days passed, Kathy's fear became well justified...

I WONDER WHERE AUNT KATHY GOES EVERY NIGHT? IF SHE'S DATING A SPECIAL PERSON, WHY DOESN'T HE EVER CALL FOR HER HERE?

...AND NOW FOR A NEWS EXCLUSIVE -- ACTUAL FILMS OF **BATWOMAN** IN ACTION -- TAKEN BY A NEWS CAMERAMAN WHO HAPPENED TO BE ON THE SCENE...

Surprising thieves robbing the safe of a manufacturer of school supplies, **BATWOMAN** instantly went into action...

AS THE THUGS FELL BACK, UPSETTING CARTONS OF GOLD STARS, *BAT-WOMAN* FOLLOWED TO MAKE THE CAPTURE!

GOLLY! SHE'S WONDERFUL! HOW I WISH I COULD BE LIKE HER!

AND SO BETTY HAD PROMPTLY SET OUT TO MAKE HER WISH COME TRUE...

BUT, BETTY--HOW-- HOW DID YOU GUESS *I* WAS *BATWOMAN?*

WHEN I BRUSHED MY HAIR WITH YOUR BRUSH, SOME *GOLD STARS* FELL OUT! I REALIZED THOSE STARS COULD ONLY HAVE GOTTEN ON IT WHEN YOU BRUSHED YOUR HAIR AFTER YOUR CAPTURE OF THOSE CROOKS!

SO I SECRETLY MADE MYSELF A COSTUME-- AND TONIGHT I TRAILED YOU!

YOU WERE VERY CLEVER, BETTY-- BUT YOU MUST NEVER BE *BAT-GIRL* AGAIN!

IF *YOU* CAN BE *BATWOMAN, I* CAN CERTAINLY BE *BAT-GIRL!* MAYBE WE CAN BE A TEAM--LIKE *BATMAN* AND *ROBIN!*

SHE HAS NO IDEA HOW DANGEROUS FIGHTING IS! I'D BETTER GET *BATMAN'S* ADVICE ON HOW TO COPE WITH BETTY!

LATER, AT POLICE HEADQUARTERS...

BETTY'S BRIGHT AND SHE LEARNS QUICKLY--BUT SHE'S ALSO VERY HEADSTRONG! WHAT CAN I DO TO DISSUADE HER?

GOSH, *BATMAN*-- AN INEXPERIENCED GIRL IS BOUND TO GET HURT PURSUING CROOKS--

THAT'S IT! SUPPOSE, *BATWOMAN,* YOU *PRETEND* YOU'LL ALLOW HER TO BE *BAT-GIRL*-- BUT ONLY AFTER A LOT OF TRAINING...

FINE! I'LL *STALL* HER BY KEEPING HER IN TRAINING UNTIL IT'S TIME FOR HER TO RETURN HOME!

THUS, SOMETIME LATER, THE DETERMINED GIRL COMES TO THE END OF HER HUNT...

JUST AS I THOUGHT--AN ABANDONED RAYON PLANT...AND THAT MUST BE THE BOSS HIMSELF-- *KING COBRA!* I--I REALLY SHOULD NOTIFY AUNT KATHY...BUT I'M *NOT!* I'LL PROVE TO HER I *AM* READY!

THIS *SELF-INFLATING* BALLOON FROM MY *CRIME COMPACT* WILL STARTLE THEM SO, I'LL BE ABLE TO LASSO THEM WITH MY *BAT-ROPE!*

-SSSSS

WH--WHAT'S THAT?

YOW!

I FOUND YOU MYSELF--AND NOW I'LL CAPTURE YOU MYSELF!

BUT, AS THE SURPRISED GANG BOSS' LIGHTED CIGAR FLIES FROM HIS HAND, IT TOUCHES THE BALLOON AND...

WHAT...?

IT EXPLODED IN HER FACE! *QUICK--GRAB HER!* IT'S THAT KID-- *BAT-GIRL*--WHO WAS RESPONSIBLE FOR OUR BOYS GETTING CAUGHT THE OTHER DAY!

MINUTES LATER...

WE'LL LOCK HER UP IN THIS OLD OFFICE--AND KEEP HER AS A HOSTAGE TO FORCE *BATMAN* TO RELEASE OUR PALS FROM JAIL!

6

ALONE NOW, *BAT-GIRL* REALIZES THE DAMAGE HER OVER-CONFIDENCE HAS CAUSED...

OH, WHAT A FOOL I'VE BEEN! THOSE CROOKS *BATMAN*, *ROBIN* AND *BATWOMAN* CAUGHT WILL BE FREED -- AND ALL BECAUSE OF ME! IF I COULD ONLY MAKE UP FOR MY MISTAKE...

HMM! THESE SHEETS OF THIN CARBON PAPER -- AND THAT VENTILATOR! I'VE GOT AN IDEA! IF I CUT THE CARBON PAPER INTO BAT-LIKE SHAPES --!

SOON AFTER, AN UPDRAFT WAFTS THE CUTOUTS TO THE ROOF'S EXHAUST VENT...

SOMETIME LATER...

HUH? THEY FOUND US, TOO!

ULP! WE'RE FINISHED!

PAPER "BATS"! IT'S SOME KIND OF *BAT-SIGNAL!* I'D BETTER CALL THE POLICE ABOUT THIS!

NOT YET! I'VE STILL GOT AN ACE! HOLD THEM OFF!

© 1961 National Periodical Publications, Inc.

THE NEXT NIGHT, HOWEVER, BAT-GIRL IS SO ANXIOUS, SHE'S AT THE MEETING PLACE EARLIER THAN USUAL...

BAT-MITE'S PLAN IS TO MAKE THE ANIMATED FIGURES LOOK LIKE GANGSTERS WHO WILL ABDUCT ME IN THE "GETAWAY CAR," JUST AS ROBIN APPROACHES! HE'LL WORRY ABOUT ME-- FIND A "CLUE"-- RESCUE ME-- AND THEN REALIZE HOW MUCH HE CARES FOR ME! I HOPE IT WORKS!

BUT, AS FATE WOULD HAVE IT--REAL THUGS SUDDENLY APPEAR, AND...

LOOK!... BAT-GIRL--ALONE! THIS IS OUR CHANCE! WE'LL GRAB HER AND TAKE HER ALONG ON OUR JOB...

YEAH--SHE'LL BE OUR "INSURANCE," IN CASE COPS TRY TO STOP US!

THINKING THEY ARE BAT-MITE'S CREATIONS, BAT-GIRL ALLOWS HERSELF TO BE EASILY OVERCOME...

QUICK--SHOVE HER INSIDE!

WAIT!.... A THIRD MAN! THAT MEANS THESE ARE REAL THUGS!

SHORTLY, WHEN THE INVISIBLE BAT-MITE ARRIVES...

BAT-GIRL SHOULD'VE BEEN HERE BY NOW! ISN'T THAT JUST LIKE A WOMAN--TO BE LATE FOR AN APPOINTMENT!

SOON, ROBIN ARRIVES--AND HE, TOO, WAITS IMPATIENTLY, UNTIL HIS KEEN EYES SPY SOMETHING...

WHY--IT'S THE BOTTLE OF LUMINOUS INK THAT BAT-GIRL KEEPS IN HER CRIME-COMPACT! THAT MEANS SHE WAS HERE--AND LEFT IT AS A CLUE! SHE'S IN TROUBLE!

YIPES! THAT EXPLAINS EVERYTHING! THIS IS AWFUL! POOR BAT-GIRL!

BAT-MITE! WHAT...?

ROBIN, I'VE A CONFESSION TO MAKE; GULP! AND I HOPE YOU WON'T BE TOO ANGRY...

POP!

AFTER EXPLAINING...

D-DO YOU THINK YOU CAN FORGIVE ME?

RIGHT NOW, I CAN ONLY THINK OF THIS BOTTLE! IT'S NEARLY EMPTY--WHICH MEANS THAT IN THE STRUGGLE, SHE MANAGED TO SPLASH THE INK ON A CAR--SO THE INK WOULD DRIP OFF AND LEAVE A LUMINOUS TRAIL!

WE'D BE ABLE TO SEE A LUMINOUS TRAIL EASIER FROM THE AIR... I'LL GET THE **WHIRLY-BAT** FROM THE **BATMOBILE!**

DON'T BOTHER... I'LL HAVE THAT **SEA GULL** GIVE US A LIFT!

WITH HIS UNCANNY MAGIC, **BAT-MITE** TURNS THE BIRD INTO A GIGANTIC CREATURE, SO THAT...

SEE THE TRAIL BETTER NOW?

YES--WE CAN'T MISS FINDING **BAT-GIRL** NOW!

LATER, AS THE BANDITS CRACK THE SAFE OF A COMPANY THAT MAKES GOLD-PLATED SPORTS TROPHIES...

THIS GOLD SUPPLY... WHAT A HAUL!

AND I'M GOING TO HAUL YOU ALL RIGHT TO JAIL!

ROBIN!

HOLD IT, **ROBIN!** YOU'RE GONNA LET US GET AWAY--OR THIS KID GETS HURT!

I CAN'T RISK **BAT-GIRL'S** SAFETY... I'VE NO CHOICE BUT TO LET THEM ESCAPE!

7

IN GOTHAM CITY, A DEADLY DRAMA IS ABOUT TO TAKE PLACE-- AND UNKNOWINGLY, FOUR APPARENTLY ORDINARY PEOPLE WILL BE THRUST INTO THE LEADING ROLES...

BRUCE WAYNE-- WEALTHY, PROMINENT SOCIALITE...

BRUCE IS A NICE, AMIABLE FELLOW-- BUT IT'S A MYSTERY TO ME WHY HE SEEMS TO HAVE NO GOAL IN LIFE!

POLICE COMMISS. GORDON

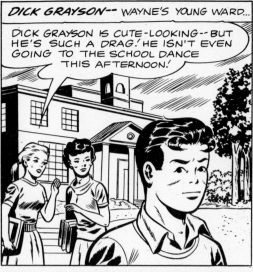

DICK GRAYSON-- WAYNE'S YOUNG WARD...

DICK GRAYSON IS CUTE-LOOKING-- BUT HE'S SUCH A DRAG! HE ISN'T EVEN GOING TO THE SCHOOL DANCE THIS AFTERNOON!

KATHY KANE-- BLESSED WITH RICHES AND BEAUTY...

I'LL NEVER UNDERSTAND WHY A WOMAN AS ATTRACTIVE AS KATHY ISN'T MARRIED YET!

BETTY KANE-- KATHY'S YOUNG NIECE, FROM OUT-OF-TOWN...

I CAN HARDLY WAIT TO SEE AUNT KATHY AGAIN! EXCITING THINGS ALWAYS HAPPEN WHEN I VISIT HER!

FOUR ORDINARY PEOPLE, WITH ORDINARY LIVES! BUT, UNKNOWN TO THE WORLD, EACH OF THEM HAS A DOUBLE LIFE!

OKAY, ROBIN --LET'S TAKE THE BATMOBILE OUT FOR A SPIN AND SEE IF ANY CRIMES NEED BUSTING!

HURRY AUNT KATHY! GOSH! I HOPE I GET A CHANCE TO SEE BATMAN AGAIN!

BATMAN? ARE YOU SURE YOU DON'T REALLY MEAN ROBIN?

2

FOUR NOT-SO-ORDINARY PEOPLE--BUT THERE IS YET ANOTHER, WHOM FATE HAS SELECTED TO CATAPULT THEM INTO FANTASTIC ADVENTURE!

NOW, FOR MY MISSION! BUT FIRST, I MUST STORE MY TELEPORTER SOMEWHERE! AH! THAT DESERTED OLD BUILDING WILL DO FINE-- THEN I'LL START MY SEARCH FOR VAUX!

SHORTLY, AS A U.S. MAIL HELICOPTER IS ON ITS WAY TOWARD A MAIL STATION...

GREAT GUNS! SOME KIND OF ALIEN BEING! I'D BETTER SEE WHERE HE'S HEADING-- AND RADIO THE POLICE IN CASE HE INTENDS TO MAKE TROUBLE!

AS THE ALIEN NEARS THE ROAD...

THE VAUX-DETECTOR IS CLICKING--INDICATING A GOOD QUANTITY OF VAUX IN THAT BUILDING AHEAD!

CLICK CLICK!

MOMENTS LATER, THE BATMOBILE DRAWS NEAR...

THAT MUST BE HIM-- THE ALIEN THE POLICE ALARM MENTIONED!

HIS STRANGE WEAPON IS DISINTEGRATING THAT WALL!

ZZZAP

AS THE ALIEN'S SLED ZOOMS INTO THE BUILDING, THE CRIME-FIGHTERS ARE CLOSE BEHIND...

HE'S HEADING FOR THE BALCONY! WE'VE GOT TO GET UP THERE FAST, ROBIN! THAT REPLICA OF A DIAMOND RING WILL TAKE US THERE!

THOSE TWO-- THEY SEEM INTENT UPON SEIZING ME!

③

274

SWIFTLY, *KARN* DRIVES HIS SLED FORWARD AT AMAZING SPEED, SNAPPING THE WIRES...

SN-A-A-P

INSTANTLY, *BATMAN* GAUGES THE DANGER--AND TRAINED REFLEXES ACT WITH THE SWIFTNESS OF THOUGHT!

ONLY CHANCE-- THAT MODEL OF A PENDANT!

VISELIKE, *BATMAN'S* HANDS GRIP THEIR TARGET, AND...

MADE IT!

I AM GLAD YOU ESCAPED INJURY--BUT I CANNOT RISK LETTING YOU CAPTURE ME!

THE ALIEN IS *"SPEAKING"* TO US BY PROJECTING HIS THOUGHTS!

I MUST STOP YOU FROM INTERFERING WITH MY MISSION!

THE WEAPON THAT DISINTEGRATED THE WALL--FIRING AT US! *UHH--UHH!*

IS THIS TO BE THE END OF *BATMAN* AND *ROBIN?*

4

MINUTES PASS, AND THEN...

HUH? WE--WE'RE ALIVE!

YEP! I SAW IT ALL! HIS WEAPON ONLY KNOCKED YOU UNCONSCIOUS!

THEN HE *DIDN'T* TRY TO DISINTEGRATE US! HE CAN VARY THE POWER OF HIS WEAPON! THE ALIEN IS A CROOK--BUT HE'S NO KILLER!

YEAH, BUT HE'S NOT MUCH OF A CROOK--BECAUSE HE DIDN'T TOUCH ANY DIAMONDS...

...ALL HE GRABBED WAS A FEW BROOCHES AND RINGS MADE OF *SILVER!*

HMM! HE'S AN ALIEN, FROM AN ALIEN WORLD! IT *IS* POSSIBLE THAT ON HIS WORLD, SILVER IS RARE--SO RARE THAT IT'S MORE PRECIOUS THAN GEMS!

MEANWHILE, AS THE *BAT-CYCLE* ROARS ALONG THE HIGHWAY...

I'LL BET THE *BATMOBILE* PICKED UP THE POLICE ALARM ABOUT THE ALIEN, AS WE DID! MAYBE WE CAN GIVE *BATMAN* AND *ROBIN* A HAND!

BATWOMAN-- LOOK! THAT MUST BE-- THE ALIEN!

AT THAT MOMENT, *BATMAN* USES HIS RADIO TO CUT IN ON THE POLICE RADIO BAND...

CALLING ALL CARS! THIS IS *BATMAN!* THE ALIEN HAS ESCAPED CAPTURE!

...WATCH ALL ROADS AND KEEP ME POSTED!

CALLING *BATMAN!* THIS IS *BATWOMAN!* *BAT-GIRL* IS WITH ME! WE JUST SIGHTED THE ALIEN ...

...RIDING UP SIMMONS LANE!

5

SHORTLY, AFTER THE TWO TEAMS OF CRIME-FIGHTERS JOIN FORCES...

SIMMONS LANE LEADS TO THE BIG *ACE FILM COMPANY* PLANT! THEY USE A *LOT* OF SILVER THERE!

RIGHT! THAT COMPANY MANUFACTURES TONS OF PHOTOGRAPHIC FILM -- AND FILM EMULSION CONTAINS SILVER CHLORIDE OR SILVER BROMIDE!

AS GUARDS ARE ABOUT TO WHEEL INGOTS OF SILVER INTO THE FILM COMPANY'S NOVEL BUILDING...

MY *VAUX-DETECTOR* HAS LED ME TO A GREAT QUANTITY OF VAUX THIS TIME!

ACE FILM COMPANY

CLICK-CLICK-CLICK

THE ONES WHO CALLED EACH OTHER *BATMAN* AND *ROBIN*! AND WITH THEM ARE TWO MASKED FEMALES! I MUST ACT QUICKLY!

I CAN'T STEER!

GREAT SCOTT! NOW HIS WEIRD GUN IS *PUSHING* THE *BAT-CYCLE* OFF-COURSE! IT'S GOING TO CRASH RIGHT INTO US!

CRACKLE

WITH LIGHTNING-LIKE REFLEXES, *BATMAN* STEPS ON THE GAS, AND THEN YANKS HARD AT THE WHEEL...

WHEW! THAT WAS CLOSE!

SCREECH

6

277

THE ALIEN'S, GETTING AWAY AGAIN

WELL, MAYBE *THIS* WILL HELP US CATCH UP TO HIM AGAIN!

TAKING AIM, *BATMAN* HEAVES THE BOTTLE AT THE SWIFT TARGET...

FOOLISH EARTHLING! YOU MISSED ME AND HIT MY ANTI-GRAVITY SLED INSTEAD!

TOO BAD, *BATMAN!*

BUT I *WANTED* TO HIT THE SLED! THAT BOTTLE CONTAINED CHEMICALS USED IN EXPERIMENTS WITH ULTRA-VIOLET LIGHT! HIS 'SLED WILL NOW LEAVE A *TRAIL OF DROPS* FOR US TO FOLLOW!

ACE FILM

SHORTLY...

THESE SPECIAL FILTER GOGGLES ENABLE ME TO SPOT THOSE DROPS!

SOMETIME LATER...

THE DROPS LED TO THAT DESERTED OLD FACTORY! WE'LL TAKE HIM BY SURPRISE!

IF HE HASN'T ALREADY SPOTTED US THROUGH A WINDOW!

BATMAN'S WORRY PROVES CORRECT, AS...

YOUR INTERFERENCE CAN JEOPARDIZE MY MISSION-- AND I MUST FIND A STOCK- PILE OF *VAUX!* NOW I AM FORCED TO TAKE DRASTIC ACTION!

GREAT SCOTT! HE'S BROUGHT A FANTASTIC MACHINE WITH HIM! *GET BACK!*

7

BEFORE THEIR HORRIFIED EYES, *BATMAN* AND *BATWOMAN* SEE *ROBIN* AND *BAT-GIRL* FADE INTO NOTHINGNESS! THEN...

TH-THEY'VE DISAPPEARED--BUT *WE'RE* STILL HERE! STRANGE-- THE ELECTRIC AURA THAT WAS ALL ABOUT US, IS GONE--AND NOW THAT IT HAS, I'M SO... SO TIRED...

I--I FEEL AS IF ALL THE ENERGY WAS DRAINED FROM ME...

AT THAT MOMENT, THE MYSTIFIED ALIEN TURNS OFF HIS MACHINE...

VERY ODD! MY *TELEPORTER* SHOULD HAVE TRANSMITTED YOU TWO TO MY DIMENSION, AS IT DID THE BOY AND THE GIRL -- YET IT DIDN'T!

BATWOMAN! DID YOU HEAR? *ROBIN* AND *BAT-GIRL* ARE ALIVE-- THEY'RE *ALIVE!*

TRYING AGAIN, *KARN* TURNS ON THE POWER OF HIS *DIMENSION-TELEPORTER,* BUT...

FOR SOME REASON, IT FAILS TO TRANSMIT YOU TWO! BUT I CAN'T WASTE TIME PUZZLING IT OUT NOW! I HAVE A MISSION TO COMPLETE!

IN THEIR STRANGELY WEAKENED CONDITION, THE CRIME-FIGHTERS ARE UNABLE TO RESIST *KARN*...

JUST TO MAKE CERTAIN YOU CANNOT ESCAPE AND INTERFERE AGAIN, I'LL LOCK YOU IN A ROOM --WHILE I RAID YOUR WORLD FOR MORE *VAUX!*

SHORTLY...

I HAVE THE STRANGEST SENSATION! I FEEL *INCOMPLETE* -- AS IF PART OF ME IS MISSING!

SOMEHOW I-- I SENSE *I'VE SPLIT INTO TWO BEINGS!*

YES! AND SOMEHOW I KNOW THAT OUR *OTHER SELVES* ARE *ELSEWHERE*-- ON SOME STRANGE WORLD!

10

AT THAT MOMENT, SOMEWHERE ON A LAND BEYOND EARTH'S SPACE AND TIME...

WH-WHAT? SOMEHOW WE'VE BEEN TRANSPORTED TO *ANOTHER WORLD!*

BATMAN! OUR FORMS HAVE CHANGED! WHAT'S HAPPENED TO US?

GREAT SCOTT! WE'VE BECOME *PURE ENERGY!* IN SOME FREAKISH WAY, THE ALIEN'S MACHINE FREED THE *ENERGY-FORCE* FROM OUR BODIES-- AND TRANSMITTED US HERE! EACH OF US HAS SPLIT INTO *TWO BEINGS!*

TH-THEN THAT MEANS OUR BODIES-- OUR FLESH-AND-BLOOD BODIES, ARE BACK ON *EARTH!*

OH, *BATMAN* -- WHAT CAN WE DO? WE'RE STRANDED ON A STRANGE WORLD! HOW CAN WE EVER GET BACK TO MERGE WITH OUR BODIES FAR AWAY ON EARTH?

I-- I DON'T KNOW!

AND ON EARTH...

WE'VE GOT TO GET OUT OF HERE-- WARN THE AUTHORITIES...

UH-HH! NO USE! CAN'T BUDGE THE DOOR! ALL MY STRENGTH IS GONE ...

WAIT! THE ALIEN DIDN'T KNOW ABOUT MY *UTILITY-BELT!* THIS VIAL OF ACID WILL DISSOLVE THE LOCK AND FREE US!

11

MEANWHILE, HOPING TO FIND HELP, THE ENERGY FORMS OF **BATMAN** AND **BATWOMAN** MOVE TOWARD THE ALIEN CITY, BUT...

BATMAN, THE BUILDINGS ARE SHATTERING!

WE'RE THE CAUSE! OUR ENERGY-FORMS ARE EMITTING POWERFUL PULSES OF FORCE THAT DESTROY ANYTHING WITHIN RANGE!

HORRIFIED BY THE CHAOS THEY HAVE UNWITTINGLY CAUSED, THE TWO **ENERGY-BEINGS** HASTILY RETREAT...

THE WINGED PEOPLE OF THIS WORLD! THEY THINK WE'RE INVADERS!

WE'VE GOT TO MAKE THEM UNDERSTAND! **PLEASE, WE MEAN NO HARM! WE COULDN'T HELP WHAT HAPPENED!**

IT'S NO USE! THEY CAN'T UNDERSTAND US!

SOLDIERS COMING! LET'S GET AWAY BEFORE WE'RE FORCED INTO A FIGHT AND OUR ENERGY BEAMS HURT THEM!

SEEKING REFUGE, **BATMAN** AND **BATWOMAN** PLUNGE INTO THE DEPTHS OF THE NEARBY WOODS, BUT...

GOOD HEAVENS! OUR PULSES OF FORCE ARE SMASHING DOWN EVERYTHING AROUND US!

NO USE! WE CAN'T HIDE! INSTEAD, WE'VE ACTUALLY LEFT A TRAIL FOR THEM TO SIGHT FROM ABOVE!

12

WARILY, THE WINGED PEOPLE KEEP BEYOND RANGE OF THE FORCE-PULSES--AND LAUNCH AN AERIAL ATTACK!

WE'RE SAFE ENOUGH! OUR AURAS OF FORCE ARE SHATTERING THEIR SPEARS!

OH, WHY CAN'T THEY UNDERSTAND THAT ALL WE WANT TO DO IS FIND A WAY BACK TO OUR OWN BODIES!

AND ON EARTH...

THE TELEPORTER! PERHAPS ITS POWER CAN PULL OUR ENERGY-SELVES BACK INTO OUR BODIES!

YOU'RE FORGETTING--WHEN THE ALIEN TURNED ITS POWER ON US A SECOND TIME, NOTHING HAPPENED! FIRST, WE MUST FIGURE OUT WHY IT WORKED ONLY ON ROBIN AND BAT-GIRL--AND NOT ON US!

MEANWHILE, IN THE OTHER WORLD--A MONSTROUS SHAPE DARKENS THE SKY!

GREAT SCOTT! A COLOSSAL BEAST--AND IT'S GOING FOR THE BIRD-PEOPLE!

THEIR SPEARS ONLY BOUNCE OFF THAT BEAST'S HIDE! BATMAN, SOMEHOW WE'VE GOT TO HELP THOSE BRAVE BEINGS!

MAYBE IF WE CONCENTRATE OUR THOUGHTS, WE CAN CONTROL OUR ENERGIES--AND FOCUS AT THAT BEAST!

THE STRATEGY WORKS--AND TWO LENGTHENING BEAMS OF FORCE STRIKE THEIR TARGET!

RAAAAAA!

13

AS THEY GRASP HANDS AND CONCENTRATE, THEIR ENERGIES FLOW TOGETHER LIKE AN ELECTRICAL CURRENT--AND *ONE THUNDERBOLT OF FORCE* STABS AT THE WINGED COLOSSUS!

THE BEAST IS HURT--BUT IT'S STILL ALIVE--AND COMING FOR *US!*

QUICK-- *GRAB MY HAND!* MAYBE WE CAN DESTROY IT-- TOGETHER!

OUR COMBINED ENERGIES DID IT!

YES--AND NOW THE BIRD-- PEOPLE ARE SMILING AT US! NOW THEY KNOW WE'RE THEIR FRIENDS!

MEANWHILE, ON EARTH-- *BATMAN* PRODS HIS TRAINED MIND...

NOW I REMEMBER! *WE* WERE STANDING ON A *MANHOLE COVER*--BUT THE YOUNGSTERS WEREN'T! IT WAS THE *STEEL* MANHOLE COVER THAT CAUSED THE FREAK REACTION!

THEN, TO DRAW THE ENERGY-- FORCES BACK INTO OUR BODIES, WE HAVE TO REPEAT WHAT HAPPENED!

EXACTLY-- BUT WE'LL HAVE TO TURN THE *TELE- PORTER'S* POWER TO *REVERSE!* COME ON, BETWEEN US, WE HAVE JUST ENOUGH STRENGTH LEFT TO CARRY THIS MACHINE TO THAT MANHOLE COVER!

14

The twin selves of BATMAN and BAT-WOMAN -- DYING--YET HOPING FOR A MIRACLE! WHAT CAN SAVE THEM NOW?

CONTINUED

MEANWHILE--WHAT HAS HAPPENED TO *BAT-GIRL* AND *ROBIN?*

TWO STRANGE BEINGS--MATERIALIZING! OBVIOUSLY KARN TELEPORTED THEM--TO OUR DIMENSION--TO KEEP THEM FROM INTERFERING WITH HIS SEARCH FOR *VAUX!*

ROBIN-- DID YOU HEAR? THIS IS THE *ALIEN'S DIMENSION!*

WHO ARE YOU? WE KNOW KARN IS AFTER *VAUX--* OR *SILVER,* AS WE CALL IT-- BUT WHY?

I AM *ZEBO--* A *SCIENTIST!* IT IS I WHO INVENTED THE DIMENSIONAL-TELEPORTER AND THE HAND-WEAPON YOU UNDOUBTEDLY SAW KARN USE!

VAUX IS VERY RARE IN OUR WORLD--BUT ONLY VAUX CAN POWER THE HAND-WEAPON I INVENTED! LUCKILY I HAD TO SEND HIM INTO YOUR DIMENSION TO SEARCH FOR MORE TO BE ABLE TO POWER *THIS!*

A REPLICA OF KARN'S WEAPON-- BUT IT'S AS *BIG AS A CANNON!*

MY SECRET WEAPON! WAR HAS BEEN OUTLAWED IN OUR WORLD FOR CENTURIES, SO THE PRESIDENT'S ARMY HAS ONLY TOKEN WEAPONS! WHEN KARN BRINGS *VAUX* BACK TO POWER MY *DISINTEGRATOR-CANNON,* I'LL DESTROY THE PRESIDENT'S MEAGER ARMY-- AND MAKE MYSELF *DICTATOR!*

UHH... WOULD ANYONE MIND IF I PUT ON A LITTLE LIPSTICK?

;HA, HA! A FEMALE IS THE SAME IN *ANY* WORLD! WHEN FACING A PROBLEM, SHE ALWAYS RESORTS TO POWDERING HER NOSE OR PUTTING ON FRESH LIPSTICK!

BUT THE "LIPSTICK" FROM *BAT-GIRL'S CRIME-COMPACT* IS GIMMICKED--AND AS SHE PRESSES A SECRET TRIGGER ...

ROBIN! DUCK!

WHAT...? IT'S SHOOTING OUT TENDRILS OF WIRE-- ENTANGLING US!

18

290

IT WORKED! THAT STICKY FLUID WILL BLIND THAT BEAST MOMENTARILY NOW-- LET'S GET OUT OF HERE!

OH, ROBIN-- YOU'RE WONDERFUL!

ON--ON THROUGH THE BIZARRE FOREST RUN THE DARING YOUNGSTERS--AS ZEBO'S MEN PURSUE!

HURRY, BAT-GIRL, HURRY!

WITHOUT WARNING...

UHHHH!

MOMENTS LATER, WHEN ROBIN REGAINS CONSCIOUSNESS...

WH-WHAT HAPPENED?

THAT PLANT ACCIDENTALLY KNOCKED YOU OUT! THAT KNOB IS REALLY A SUCKER-DISC--AND IT SHOOTS OUT TO ABSORB WATER!

OH, I'M SO GLAD YOU'RE ALL RIGHT! I WAS SO WORRIED ABOUT YOU...

GOSH! YOU WERE? GEE, BAT-GIRL... I--I...

MMMMMMM!

20

291

HOOF BEATS! ZEBO'S MEN ARE GETTING CLOSER!

CLOP CLOP CLOP

RUSHING ONWARD, THEY SUDDENLY COME UPON A GLITTERING EXPANSE...

A FIELD OF MICA CRYSTALS! THAT STUFF IS AS SLIPPERY AS SNOW!

SAY--IF WE COULD TOBOGGAN DOWN THAT MICA, WE'D MAKE BETTER TIME THAN IF WE RAN DOWN THE SLOPE THROUGH THE FOREST!

MINUTES LATER...

NOT BAD, EH? THESE BIG LEAVES MAKE GREAT SLEDS!

BUT SHORTLY AFTER...

OH, NO! A LAKE! WE COULD NEVER SWIM ACROSS FAST ENOUGH-- AND IF WE CIRCLE AROUND IT THROUGH THE FOREST, ZEBO'S MEN WILL CATCH UP TO US!

CLOP CLOP CLOP

HMM! A LAKE IN FRONT--AND THOSE WATER-SUCKING PLANTS BEHIND US! I'VE GOT AN IDEA...

THE YOUNGSTERS WORK SWIFTLY--THEN WAIT FOR THEIR PURSUERS TO CLOSE IN!

THERE THEY ARE -- WAITING FOR US! THEY ARE GIVING THEMSELVES UP!

OKAY, BAT-GIRL-- NOW!

21

INSTANTLY, THE YOUNGSTERS HURL WATER-FILLED PLANT CUPS FORWARD...

WHAT...?

...AND THE GREEDY SUCKER-DISCS ON BOTH SIDES OF THE GROVE, SHOOT OUT TOWARD THE SPLASHES OF WATER!

UHHH!

WHAT...?! I'M CAUGHT-- TANGLED IN THESE VINES!

ONE OF THEM GOT FREE!

WE COULD USE HIS "HORSE"! COME ON, BAT-GIRL!

AND OUT! NICE TEAMWORK, PARTNER!

UP...

THEN...

NOW WE'LL GET TO THE CITY FAST-- AND ALERT THE AUTHORITIES TO ZEBO'S PLANS! HANG ON, BAT-GIRL!

DON'T WORRY, I AM!

22

SHORTLY AFTER...

WHAT...? GOVERNMENT TROOPS! THOSE YOUNGSTERS DID GET TO THE PRESIDENT, AFTER ALL!

ONLY ONE THING I CAN DO NOW-- TELEPORT MYSELF TO JOIN KARN, AND HIDE IN EARTH'S DIMENSION!

ZEBO--FADING AWAY! HE'S TELEPORTING HIMSELF TO EARTH!

MEANWHILE, ON EARTH, *BATMAN* HAS THOUGHT OF A PLAN, AND ACTS ON IT!

AT LEAST OUR WEIGHT... AND REMAINING STRENGTH... IS ENOUGH TO TIP OVER THIS MACHINE A BIT...

LUCKILY... THERE WERE A FEW OLD SKATES... LEFT BEHIND... IN THIS DEFUNCT ROLLER SKATE FACTORY! KEEP THE *TELEPORTER* BALANCED... WHILE I... SLIP TWO SKATES UNDER THE CORNERS... ON THIS SIDE...

UPON REPEATING THE PROCESS, AND TYING THE SKATES TO THE CORNERS, *BATMAN* AND *BATWOMAN* SUMMON UP THEIR REMAINING STRENGTH TO PUSH THE TELEPORTER OUT OF THE FACTORY...

OH... SO TIRED... SO TIRED...

DON'T STOP NOW... GOT TO KEEP GOING... THE MANHOLE COVER... ONLY A FEW YARDS AWAY FROM US NOW...

AT THAT MOMENT, AS KARN NEARS HIS HIDEOUT WITH SILVER HE HAS JUST STOLEN...

ZEBO --HERE! WHAT'S HAPPENED?

EVERYTHING! BECAUSE OF THOSE TWO YOUNGSTERS YOU SENT TO OUR DIMENSION, OUR PLANS ARE RUINED!

23

AS ZEBO EXPLAINS, SUDDENLY...

LOOK! THEY FOLLOWED ME HERE! DISINTEGRATE THEM!

GLADLY! PREVIOUSLY, I WANTED TO CONSERVE THE WEAPON'S POWER, AND THEREFORE WAS MERCIFUL--BUT NOW I WILL TURN IT TO FULL POWER!

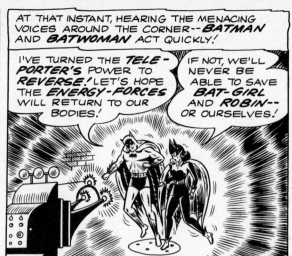

AT THAT INSTANT, HEARING THE MENACING VOICES AROUND THE CORNER--BATMAN AND BATWOMAN ACT QUICKLY!

I'VE TURNED THE TELE-PORTER'S POWER TO REVERSE! LET'S HOPE THE ENERGY-FORCES WILL RETURN TO OUR BODIES!

IF NOT, WE'LL NEVER BE ABLE TO SAVE BAT-GIRL AND ROBIN-- OR OURSELVES!

IN THAT SPLIT-INSTANT, ON THE OTHER WORLD...

BATMAN--SOME POWER IS TUGGING AT ME!

WE'RE SAVED! WE'RE GOING BACK! WE'RE GOING BACK!

AND, SUDDENLY, ON EARTH, BATMAN AND BATWOMAN ARE REVITALIZED--COMPLETE BEINGS AGAIN!

THAT DYING BEAST DRAINED OFF SOME OF OUR NORMAL STRENGTH -- BUT WE'VE GOT MORE THAN ENOUGH TO HANDLE THOSE TWO ALIENS!

WHAT...?

NOW I FEEL LIKE MY OLD SELF AGAIN!

24

Art:
Irv Novick
&
Dick Giordano
Story:
Frank Robbins

BATMAN
"ONE BULLET TOO MANY!"

A DESPERATELY LONELY DAY IN THE LIFE OF **BRUCE WAYNE**, GUARDIAN AND FRIEND TO YOUNG **DICK GRAYSON**... A DAY ALWAYS DREADED... ALWAYS EXPECTED ... BUT NEVER QUITE PREPARED FOR ...

ALL HERE---AS IT **USED** TO **BE!** BUT---NO LONGER THE SAME...

S-217

DIDN'T THINK I'D TAKE IT **THIS** HARD!

YOU NEVER KNOW--- TILL IT'S **TOO LATE!**

SAME MESSY HABITS---EVEN TO THE END! SLOPPY KID---AND I'M ≷SNIFFLE≷ GETTING EVEN SLOPPIER!

GOT TO FACE UP TO IT--NO MATTER HOW IT HURTS! FROM NOW ON, *EVERYTHING* IS GOING TO BE *DIFFERENT*---IT *HAS* TO BE...

HARUMPH ≷SNUFFLE≷ SORRY TO BREAK IN ON YOUR---*OUR* PRIVATE SORROWS, MASTER BRUCE, BUT...

YES, ALFRED---WHAT IS IT?

ALL ≷SNIFF≷ ALL IS IN READINESS, SIR! IT IS TIME TO GO DOWN...

AW, C'MON, FELLAS---WE'RE *ALL* GROWN UP NOW! STOP ACTING LIKE YOU'RE ATTENDING MY---*FUNERAL!*

2

I KNOW IT'S GOING TO BE PRETTY ROUGH ON YOU GUYS--- IN THE *BEGINNING!* GUESS IT'S KINDA HARD FOR YOU TO DIG THAT ONLY *YESTERDAY...*

...I WAS *YOUR* "YOUNG MASTER DICK," ALFIE...

...AND *YOUR* "KID WHO NEEDED A BIG-BROTHER-IMAGE," BRUCE...

BUT---I'M A *MAN* NOW!

'LEAST---THAT'S WHAT MY DRAFT-CARD SAYS...

...PLUS MY ACCEPTANCE AT *HUDSON UNIVERSITY!*

SO... I'D PREFER TO GO TO THE AIRPORT---*ALONE...*

I--I HATE--- *LONG* GOOD-BYES!

AND SUDDENLY A BIG, UNDER-OCCUPIED *WAYNE MANOR* BECOMES VASTER... EMPTIER!

ALFRED, YOU KNOW ALL *THIS* JUST ISN'T GOING TO WORK ANY MORE--- NOT THE WAY IT USED TO BE!

I---I KNOW, MASTER BRUCE--- IT'S JUST TOO BIG FOR THE TWO OF US!

AND WITH YOUNG MASTER DI--ER... *MASTER* GRAYSON... COMING HOME ONLY ON OCCASIONAL WEEK ENDS AND HOLIDAYS---

AS THEY TAKE THE SECRET *BATCAVE* ELEVATOR...

WELL, WE CAN'T SAY THIS CAME AS A *SURPRISE!* I'VE THOUGHT A LOT--- PREPARED...

IT'S TIME WE *ALL* STARTED A *NEW* WAY OF LIFE! A NEW WAY OF *EVERYTHING!*

M-MASTER BRUCE-- YOU DON'T MEAN-- YOU *CAN'T!* B-BATM---

YES---*BATMAN TOO!*

DICK'S LEAVING BROUGHT HOME THE STARK FACT THAT OUR *PRIVATE* WORLD HAS CHANGED!

WE'RE IN GRAVE DANGER OF BECOMING ---*OUTMODED! OBSOLETE* DODOS OF THE *MOD WORLD* OUTSIDE!

OUR BEST CHANCE FOR SURVIVAL IS TO---*CLOSE UP SHOP* HERE!

4

LATER...

I--I CAN'T BEAR TO LOOK BACK, MASTER BRUCE!

DON'T, ALFRED--- THE FUTURE IS AHEAD!

A LONG DRIVE INTO THE CENTER OF GOTHAM, AND...

OUR NEW HOME -- WAYNE FOUNDATION!

AND THIS PENTHOUSE IS OUR "DIGS"--- CONVERTED FROM FORMER EXECUTIVE OFFICES!

MUCH BETTER BACHELOR ACCOMMODATIONS, SIR---SIMPLER TO KEEP IN ORDER! I APPROVE...

GLAD YOU DO, ALF! WE MAY HAVE TO DO A LOT OF "LEANING ON EACH OTHER" IN DAYS TO COME!

ESPECIALLY SINCE NOW-- AS BRUCE WAYNE-- I'LL BE KEEPING A CLOSER EYE ON FOUNDATION AFFAIRS BY DAY...

... AND "SOCKIN' IT TO 'EM " BY NIGHT!

AND THIS IS WHERE BATMAN AND THE WAYNE FOUNDATION START TO JOIN FORCES! READ IT, ALF--- ONE OF A SERIES OF CRUSADING ARTICLES!

"V.A.-- VICTIMS ANONYMOUS--- PART 3, BY MARLA MANNING."

6

"...LATEST VICTIM IN THE UNSUNG CASE-HISTORY OF INNOCENTS IN THE WAR AGAINST CRIME--- *DR. SUSAN FIELDING*, PEDIATRICIAN..."

"...AND WIFE *OF DR. JONAH FIELDING*, SLAIN LAST WEEK WHILE TREATING AN UNKNOWN GUN-SHOT PATIENT! IN THIS UNSOLVED TRAGEDY..."

"UNSOLVED"--- THE CRIMINAL *UNPUNISHED!* THINK OF IT, ALF...

...HOW MANY UNDERWORLD KILLINGS--MAIMINGS ---IN THIS VAST CITY LEAVE A TRAIL OF INNOCENT VICTIMS OF THE "VICTIM"! WIVES-- MOTHERS--CHILDREN...

...MANY LEFT WITH- OUT ANY MEANS OF SUPPORT! IT'S THE GREAT *UNPUBLICIZED TRAGEDY* OF OUR TIME!

WE SUFFER GREAT PAIN OVER *TRUE* JUSTICE --- *"RIGHTS OF THE INDIVIDUAL"* --- *"INNOCENT UNTIL PROVEN GUILTY"...*

...ALL FOR THE *ACCUSED* PARTIES! BUT WHAT ABOUT THE *"PROVEN"* INNOCENT-- THE *VICTIMS?*

INNOCENT VICTIMS SUCH AS *DICK* AND *I* WERE-- WHEN *OUR* PARENTS WERE BRUTALLY SLAIN! THEIR *DEATHS* WERE THE *BIRTHS* OF--- *BATMAN* AND *ROBIN!*

WE WERE IN THE FORTUNATE POSITION TO CLAIM JUSTICE FOR *OURSELVES* --- BUT WHAT OF THE LESS FORTUNATES?

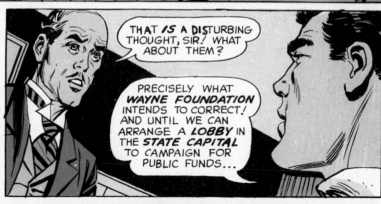

THAT *IS* A DISTURBING THOUGHT, SIR! WHAT ABOUT THEM?

PRECISELY WHAT *WAYNE FOUNDATION* INTENDS TO CORRECT! AND UNTIL WE CAN ARRANGE A *LOBBY* IN THE *STATE CAPITAL* TO CAMPAIGN FOR PUBLIC FUNDS...

...WE'RE SETTING UP A *SPECIAL ASSISTANCE PROGRAM* HERE TO AID THESE PEOPLE!

WORTHY IDEA, SIR! WHILE THESE POOR VICTIMS ARE FORGOTTEN BY THE PUBLIC--- TO *US* THEY'RE *VERY IMPOR- TANT PEOPLE! V.I.P.'S,* YOU MIGHT SAY!

7

BRILLIANT, ALF! THAT'S WHAT WE'LL NAME IT--- V.I.P. ...VICTIMS, INC. PROGRAM!

SNAP!

ALL BIG AMBITIOUS PROGRAMS HAVE TO START SMALL---

SO I'M STARTING WITH A SMALL -- BUT IMPORTANT --- PERSON, DR. SUSAN FIELDING!

A SHORT TIME LATER...

"DR. S. FIELDING ...DR. J. FIELDING"--- A HUSBAND-WIFE TEAM ON A MODEST NEIGHBORHOOD LEVEL!

DR.S.FIELD DR.J.FIELD

POOR GAL, THE TRAGEDY'S SO FRESH --- HIS SHINGLE IS STILL UP!

AS BRUCE ENTERS THE UNATTENDED OFFICE...

YOU'RE OBVIOUSLY NOT A PATIENT! OUR--MY PRACTICE IS STRICTLY WITH CHILDREN!

WHAT MORE DO YOU PEOPLE WANT OF ME? I'VE ALREADY ANSWERED ALL YOUR QUESTIONS -- OVER AND OVER...

8

I---I SHOULDN'T ⧙SOB⧘ BE DOING THIS! I ⧙SOB⧘ DON'T EVEN *KNOW* YOU!

I COULD BE A *FRIEND*-- IF YOU'LL *LET* ME!

⧙SNIFF⧘ THANKS! WHO... WHO ARE YOU?

BRUCE WAYNE --HEAD OF *WAYNE FOUNDATION!* WE WANT TO AID PEOPLE LIKE YOU--- VICTIMS OF INJUSTICE...

I DON'T NEED YOUR *CHARITY!* AND WITH ALL YOUR WEALTH --YOU CAN'T BRING JONAH BACK!

BUT *YOU* HAVE A FUTURE AHEAD OF YOU, *SERVING* MANKIND---*IF* YOU WANT TO FACE IT!

WE'RE NOT "DO-GOODERS" --- WE WANT TO *HELP!*

JUST BEFORE, YOU INDICATED THAT YOU'RE IN *DEBT!* BOTH OF YOU HAD BEEN OPERATING ON A SHOE-STRING, I GATHER?

WE WORKED OUR WAY THROUGH MEDICAL SCHOOL, WHERE WE MET--- SET UP JOINT-PRACTICE HERE WHEN WE MARRIED...

...SCRIMPING FOR OUR NEXT TEN YEARS TOGETHER TO BUY PROPER EQUIPMENT...TO TEND TO OUR LITTLE PATIENTS' NEEDS, *PROPERLY!* BUT NOW...

NOW THE CREDITORS WON'T PUT *SENTIMENT* BEFORE *CASH*, EH?

DR. J. FIELDING
DR. S. FIELDING

SO SUPPOSE *WAYNE FOUNDATION* EXTENDS YOU AN INDEFINITE-PERIOD *LOAN* WITH *NO* INTEREST CHARGES? *THAT* WOULDN'T BE CHARITY---

BUT IT WOULD MAKE YOU AWFUL DARN --- FOOLS, I GUESS!

BUT, YES --*YES!* I ACCEPT YOUR OFFER!

THEN *THAT'S* SETTLED! WISH *WE* COULD FIND YOUR HUSBAND'S *KILLER* AS EASILY!

HOW COULD *YOU---* WHEN EVEN THE *POLICE* ARE UP AGAINST A BLANK WALL?

I HAVE A---*FRIEND*--WHO SPECIALIZES IN "BLANK-WALL CASES" --- *BATMAN!*

YOU *KNOW* HIM? BUT WHY WOULD *HE---* I MEAN, THIS CASE IS SO *UNIMPORTANT* TO SUCH A BRILLIANT CRIME-FIGHTER...

YOU DON'T KNOW HIM--- LIKE *I* DO, SUSAN! *ALL* HUMANITY IS IMPORTANT TO *BATMAN--ANY* LIFE, NO MATTER HOW INSIGNIFICANT IN THE PUBLIC EYE!

CARE TO TELL ME ABOUT IT?

JONAH AND I SPLIT OUR OFFICE-HOURS-- I RAN AN *AFTER-HOURS* SESSION FOR WORKING-MOTHERS AND THEIR CHILDREN...

"ON THAT...FATAL..NIGHT, I HAD JUST TURNED IN, EXHAUSTED FROM A FULL SCHEDULE ...WHEN THERE CAME THAT INSISTENT RINGING OF OUR FRONT-DOOR BELL..."

WHO COULD *THAT* BE?

YOU'VE *HAD* IT, HONEY--- *I'LL* TAKE IT! PROBABLY SOME HYSTERICAL MOTHER WITH AN "EMERGENCY" CASE OF STOMACHITIS--

"JUST COULDN'T RESIST CHECKING... EITHER MY PROFESSIONAL TRAINING... OR PLAIN WOMAN'S CURIOSITY! AND I SAW..."

SAW *WHAT*, SUSAN?

A BIG MAN -- OBVIOUSLY IN *TROUBLE!* A TRAIL OF BLOOD -- MY HUSBAND HELPING HIM IN! COULDN'T SEE HIS *FACE...*

WAS HE *LIMPING?* HOLDING HIS LEG?

NOT THAT I NOTICED!

HMM -- THE PAPER SAID THE *KILLER* WAS A *GUN-SHOT* VICTIM --- AND SINCE EVERY DOCTOR *HAS* TO REPORT SUCH CASES TO THE POLICE...

...THE PATIENT MUST HAVE MURDERED JONAH -- *AFTER* EMERGENCY TREATMENT -- TO PREVENT *IDENTIFICATION!*

IN WHICH CASE, THERE'S A KILLER-AT-LARGE -- STILL SUFFERING A *BULLET INJURY!* AND IF HE *LIMPED* --- WE'D HAVE SOME CLUE TO START ON!

GO ON, SUSAN!

"*I* WAS BACK IN BED, FITFULLY TRYING TO SLEEP... *WHEN IT CAME!* TWO HORRIBLE *GUN-BLASTS* DOWNSTAIRS... A DOOR SLAMMING! FEARFULLY, I RAN DOWN AND..."

I -- I DIDN'T HAVE TO BE A DOCTOR TO -- *KNOW!* HE'D DIED --- *INSTANTLY!*

EASY, GAL! I KNOW HOW PAINFUL IT STILL IS...

AND THE -- PATIENT?

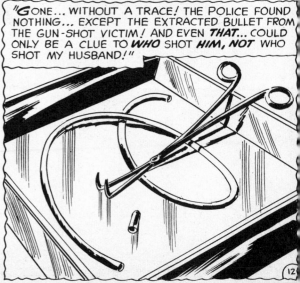

"*G*ONE... WITHOUT A TRACE! THE POLICE FOUND NOTHING... EXCEPT THE EXTRACTED BULLET FROM THE GUN-SHOT VICTIM! AND EVEN *THAT*... COULD ONLY BE A CLUE TO *WHO* SHOT *HIM*, *NOT* WHO SHOT MY HUSBAND!"

12

SO YOU SEE, BRUCE, HOW *FRUITLESS* IT ALL IS! THAT BULLET---THE *ONLY* CLUE---DOESN'T TELL US *WHO* SHOT *JONAH!*

EXCEPT THAT THE KILLER HAD TO LEAVE AS HE CAME---*WOUNDED!*

ANY WAY OF KNOWING--- HOW *BADLY* HE WAS SHOT? THE POLICE MAY BE LOOKING FOR A MAN ---*ALREADY DEAD!*

THERE WAS THAT *TOURNIQUET!*..

INDICATING HE WAS SHOT IN AN *EXTREMITY* --ARM OR LEG!

AND SINCE HE WASN'T *LIMPING* WHEN HE CAME IN--- WE'RE LOOKING FOR A KILLER WITH HIS *ARM* IN A *SLING!*

BUT--GO LOOK FOR AN UNKNOWN MAN WITH A SLING--AMONG EIGHT-MILLION FACELESS PEOPLE! WOULDN'T CHECK INTO A HOSPITAL---PROBABLY HOLED UP SOMEWHERE NURSING HIS ARM, *ALONE!*

THINK OF SOMETHING, BRUCE?

THINK I BETTER TURN THIS INFO OVER TO *BATMAN*-- IT'S ABOVE *MY* HEAD! I'LL KEEP IN TOUCH, SUSAN!

PLEASE DO, BRUCE! I'M SO GRATEFUL-- FOR EVERYTHING!

MINUTES LATER, AT THE SOUND OF A DOOR OPENING...

W-WHO'S THERE?

BATMAN?! YOU-- YOU DON'T WASTE MUCH TIME, DO YOU?

NOT WHEN *TIME* IS OF THE ESSENCE, DR. FIELDING! AND MY FRIEND, BRUCE WAYNE, JUST TOLD ME THIS TRAIL IS GETTING *COLD*...

... WHAT THERE IS OF IT! I NEED *YOUR* HELP!

YOU AND BRUCE MAKE QUITE A *TEAM,* BATMAN! I NEED *HIS* HELP--- AND *YOU* NEED *MINE!*

WHAT COULD I POSSIBLY DO?

DECOY YOUR HUSBAND'S KILLER--- BACK *HERE!*

W-WHAT...? IS THAT THE "HELP" YOU NEED--- MY *LIFE?*

LET'S LEVEL-- AND GET IT STRAIGHT! WITHOUT *YOU*-- I AND THE ENTIRE POLICE FORCE-- DON'T STAND A CHANCE...

...OF FINDING THE UNKNOWN ASSASSIN! HE'S *BURROWED* UNDER, LIKE A RAT, NURSING HIS *WOUND* SOMEWHERE IN THIS VAST CITY--- AND ONLY *ONE THING* WILL BRING HIM *OUT...*

THE *FEAR* THAT HE *HASN'T* KILLED THE *ONLY* WITNESS TO HIS *IDENTITY!*

B-BUT HE ≶SOB≶ *DID!* ONLY *JONAH* COULD'VE...

BUT *HE* DOESN'T KNOW THAT! SUPPOSE... HE GOT THE IDEA THAT *YOU* ALSO SAW HIS FACE...

...AND SOONER OR LATER, WHEN YOU GOT OVER YOUR TERROR-- YOU'D *DESCRIBE* HIM TO THE POLICE?

HE'D COME *HERE*-- AND DO TO *ME* WHAT HE DID TO ≶ SOB ≶

PRECISELY! BUT IF I STAKE-OUT AND *WAIT* FOR HIM...

I REALIZE THERE'S SOME SMALL *RISK* INVOLVED, BUT--- IF YOU *TRUST* ME?

IT-- IT'S NOT *FAIR* TO LET *JONAH'S* DEATH GO-- *UNPUNISHED!*

14

WITH SUSAN'S GO-AHEAD, *BATMAN* WASTES NO TIME! BECOMING A MAN OF A "THOUSAND FACES"...

HEAR TELL THAT DOC'S WIFE GOT HER GLIMS ON THE JOKER WHAT PUT THE SLUG INTA HER BETTER-HALF... *HEH!*

MAY HEAVEN SMILE ON YER, SON!

PASS THE WORD-- THE GAL MEDIC IS ABOUT TO SPILL!

BLIND

TAXI

NEVER TRUST A WOMAN T'KEEP HER BIG MOUTH SHUT, BUB! Y'HEAR ABOUT THAT FIELDING BABE...

AND IN THE EARLY HOURS OF DAWN...

KNOWING THE SPEED OF THE UNDERWORLD GRAPEVINE, ALFRED-- BY TONIGHT OUR BOY SHOULD BE *REAL* WORRIED...

...AND I'LL BE *WAITING* FOR HIM!

CONTINUED | 15

WHO DONE IT? WHO IS IT?

GIANTS OF THE COSMIC RAY!

FROM BEYOND THE UNKNOWN

JAN! NO. 2   15¢

DISCOVER THE AMAZING ANSWERS IN THESE LATEST DC HITS!

The WORLD'S GREATEST SUPER-HEROES!

JUSTICE LEAGUE of AMERICA

DEC. NO. 77   15¢

SUPERMAN / BATMAN / FLASH / BLACK CANARY / GREEN LANTERN / ATOM / GREEN ARROW

YOU FOOLS! I AM THE *LAST* ONE YOU'D SUSPECT OF...

BETRAYING THE JUSTICE LEAGUE!

ON SALE OCT. 23RD

ON SALE OCT 28TH

313

THAT NIGHT...

UP HERE I'VE GOT GOOD COVERAGE OF *ALL* APPROACHES TO DR. FIELDING'S OFFICE! AND CAN'T *MISS* A MAN WITH A *SLING!*

HOURS OF PATIENT WAITING LATER...

THAT'S THE LAST OF SUSAN'S APPOINTMENTS FOR TONIGHT--KEPT AN ACCURATE HEAD-COUNT AS THEY WENT IN!

WHICH UNDOUBTEDLY THE KILLER DID *TOO*--- WHEREVER HE'S HIDING!

HE'S GOT TO MAKE HIS MOVE SOON--- WHEN HE'S SURE SHE'LL BE *ALONE!*

WHO'S THIS...?

SORRY TO COME SO LATE, DOCTOR-- BUT MY LITTLE BOY---

GUESS NATURE DOESN'T KEEP DOCTOR'S HOURS, EH? COME IN...

JUST ANOTHER LI'L PATIENT-- AND HIS PA SURE HAS NO SLING!

IN HERE, PLEASE...

OKAY, KID-- YOU GOT YOUR QUARTER! COP A WALK!

:GASP:

16

BUT EVEN AS THE GUNMAN FIRES, *BATMAN* MAKES A SACRIFICE INTERCEPT, AND...

B-BATMAN?

ARGH-H!

AND AT THAT MOMENT...

SO I GOT *BATMAN FIRST!* TOUGH, SISTER--- YOU STILL GET IT...

HEY, WHAT'S THAT...?!

SOME SNOOPY NEIGHBOR MUST'VE HEARD MY EARLIER SHOT --CALLED THE FUZZ! GOTTA LAM...

AS ONE POLICEMAN GIVES CHASE...

WHAT'S GOING ON HERE?

BATMAN...? DR. FIELDING-- IS IT BAD?

DON'T KNOW YET! BETTER RUSH HIM TO A HOSPITAL!

NEGATIVE, SUSAN! I---I WANT THIS BULLET OUT *NOW!*

B-BUT--*WHY?*

20

BECAUSE THIS JOLT SHOCKED ME INTO THE REALIZATION THAT...

THE WHOLE *ANSWER* TO THIS MYSTERY DEPENDS ON *IDENTIFICATION* OF THIS *BULLET!*

*A*ND AFTER A QUICK PREPARATION...

THIS "LOCAL" MAY NOT DULL ALL THE PAIN, *BATMAN*...

NO MATTER! GET IT OUT, SUSAN--- *INTACT!*

MY... MY FIRST *DOUBT*, THAT WE WEREN'T LOOKING FOR THE *RIGHT* MAN, CAME WHEN...

WHEN...THAT *SHORT* GUNMAN TOOK THE BAIT AFTER OUR "LEAK" THAT YOU, SUSAN, COULD IDENTIFY THE "KILLER"...

YET...THE GUN-SHOT VICTIM YOU GLIMPSED WAS A "BIG" MAN!

AND... THIS SMALL JOKER WAS *HEALTHY* AND STRONG AS AN OX! NOT THE "INVALID" WE EXPECTED!

OW-TCH!

GOT IT...

YOU MEAN--THERE WERE *TWO* MEN? BUT I ONLY SAW *ONE*...

BEFORE YOU WENT BACK TO BED! BUT SUPPOSE "SHORTY" JOINED THE PARTY-- BEFORE YOUR HUSBAND WAS SHOT!

LOST HIM...! AND DIDN'T GET AN EFFECTIVE I.D.--

TOO BAD--BUT THIS SLUG MAY PUT THE FINGER ON HIM! TAKE US TO THE CRIME- LAB--- FAST!

ODD--- *I* END UP THE "MAN WITH HIS ARM IN A SLING"!

IN THE *GOTHAM CITY LIBRARY* AFTER CLOSING HOURS, BARBARA GORDON, LIBRARIAN AND DAUGHTER OF POLICE COMMISSIONER GORDON, IS IN STITCHES ...

LOOK AT THE TIME! I BETTER FINISH MY COSTUME FOR THE *POLICEMAN'S MASQUERADE BALL* TONIGHT--AND GET GOING!

SHORTLY, SHE SLIPS INTO A LARGE CLOSET WHICH SHE HAS CONVERTED INTO A DRESSING ROOM ...

THE WHOLE WORLD THINKS I'M JUST A PLAIN JANE--A COLORLESS FEMALE 'BRAIN'! I'LL SHOW THEM A FAR MORE IMPOSING GIRL TONIGHT!

A STARTLING TRANS-FORMATION ...

WELL!!! THIS "BATGIRL" COSTUME REALLY *DOES* THINGS FOR ME! I CAN HARDLY WAIT FOR THE MID-NIGHT UNMASKING HOUR-- AND THE *SHOCK* I'LL GIVE DAD!

SOON SHE IS DRIVING ALONG THE SUBURBAN HIGHWAY TOWARD THE HOTEL WHERE THE MASQUE BALL IS BEING HELD...

I MADE MY *PH.D.* AT *GOTHAM STATE UNIVERSITY*! I GRADUATED *SUMMA CUM LAUDE*! I WEAR A BROWN BELT AT JUDO! BUT TO-NIGHT WILL BE THE HIGHLIGHT OF MY LIFE!

NOT FAR AHEAD, ALONG THE SAME ROAD...

HERE COMES BRUCE WAYNE IN HIS LIMOUSINE NOW--RIGHT ON TIME!

YEAH! HE WORKS LATE AT HIS *WAYNE FOUNDATION* THE SAME NIGHT EVERY WEEK!

GLISTENING STRANDS OF GOOEY SUB-STANCE LEAP FROM THE WEAPONS OF THE MOTH-MEN -- WRAP THE WAYNE LIMOUSINE IN COCOON-LIKE FOLDS...

WE STOPPED IT COLD! NOW LET'S KNOCK WAYNE THE SAME WAY!

ZZZZZ!

EVEN AS A DOOR OF THE LIMOUSINE IS OPENED AND MILLIONAIRE BRUCE WAYNE YANKED OUT...

OHHH! COSTUMED MEN GANGING UP ON THAT DRIVER! I'VE GOT TO HELP HIM!

SCREEE!

WHY--THAT'S BRUCE WAYNE THEY'RE ATTACK-ING--DADDY'S MILLIONAIRE FRIEND! HE'S ALWAYS RE-GARDED ME AS A MOUSEY SORT OF PERSON! I WONDER WHAT HE'D SAY IF HE KNEW WHO IT WAS COMING TO RESCUE HIM! I'LL DIS-GUISE MY VOICE--SO HE DOESN'T RECOGNIZE IT!

MAKE A RUN FOR IT, MR. WAYNE-- BEFORE YOU GET HURT! BATGIRL WILL HANDLE THESE HUMAN MOTHS!

WHO'S THIS?

THAT'S A BREAK! IT'LL GIVE ME A CHANCE TO RUN JUST FAR ENOUGH TO CHANGE INTO MY BATMAN COSTUME UNOBSERVED! THAT--er--NEW BATGIRL MAY NOT BE AS GOOD AS SHE THINKS SHE IS!

I'M A FIRST KYU JUDO EXPERT, BOYS-- AS I'M WILLING TO DEMONSTRATE!

HEYY! WHATTA WE GOT HOLD OF HERE?

YA MEAN-- WHAT'S GOT HOLD OF US!

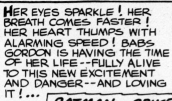

HER EYES SPARKLE! HER BREATH COMES FASTER! HER HEART THUMPS WITH ALARMING SPEED! BABS GORDON IS HAVING THE TIME OF HER LIFE--FULLY ALIVE TO THIS NEW EXCITEMENT AND DANGER--AND LOVING IT!...

BATMAN--BRUCE WAYNE IS IN DEADLY DANGER! THOSE MOTH-MEN WERE ABOUT TO BEAT HIM UP WHEN I HAPPENED ALONG! KILLER MOTH IS BOUND TO TRY AGAIN...

I'LL TAKE PERSONAL CHARGE OF BRUCE WAYNE, MA'AM! BUT WHO ARE YOU? HOW COME YOU'RE WEARING THAT-- THAT BATGIRL COSTUME?

I WAS GOING TO THE POLICEMEN'S BALL-- BUT I CAN'T NOW! MY COSTUME'S A MESS! AS FOR MY SECRET IDENTITY--I'LL EXCHANGE MINE FOR YOURS...

NO DEAL!

I THOUGHT NOT!

FOR ALL I KNOW THIS MARKS THE DEBUT AND FAREWELL APPEARANCE OF BATGIRL! IT WAS FUN WHILE IT LASTED...

NEXT DAY, DR. BARBARA GORDON TRIES TO LOSE HERSELF IN THE MUNDANE WORLD OF THE LIBRARY...

I ALMOST WISH I'D NEVER MADE THAT BATGIRL COSTUME! NOW MY LIFE SEEMS EMPTY AND HUMDRUM! I HOPE BATMAN IS GUARDING BRUCE WAYNE-- AND I WISH I WERE THERE TO HELP...

BATMAN, OF COURSE, IS BRUCE WAYNE--AND ON THIS SAME MORNING HE IS READING HIS MAIL WHEN...

HMMM-- I THOUGHT AT FIRST THAT KILLER MOTH SUSPECTED BRUCE WAYNE WAS BATMAN-- BUT THIS LETTER EXPLAINS WHY BRUCE WAYNE WAS ATTACKED LAST NIGHT!

WELL? DON'T STOP NOW!

HIS WARD DICK (ROBIN) GRAYSON LISTENS EAGERLY AS...

THIS LETTER IS FROM KILLER MOTH--TELLING ME THAT WHAT HAPPENED TO ME AS BRUCE WAYNE LAST NIGHT WAS JUST A SAMPLE OF WHAT WILL HAPPEN-- UNLESS I PAY HIM $100,000 IN CASH TONIGHT!

WOWW! THE OLD PROTECTION RACKET--IN SPADES!

IF IT HADN'T BEEN FOR THAT MYSTERIOUS BATGIRL, YOU MIGHT HAVE HAD A TOUGH TIME FIGHTING THEM OFF AS BRUCE WAYNE--

I WONDER IF KILLER MOTH CAN BE PREY-ING ON OTHER GOTHAM CITY MILLIONAIRES? THIS MAY BE A JOB FOR BATMAN AND ROBIN--SO LET'S GO!

SOON, A SECRET VISIT TO THE HOME OF MILLIONAIRE BURTON TALBOT...

I'D NEVER TELL THIS TO THE POLICE BECAUSE KILLER MOTH WARNED ME OF THE CONSEQUENCES-- BUT I CAN CONFIDE IN YOU, BATMAN! YES-- I WAS BRUTALLY BEATEN UP AND I DID PAY OUT THAT $100,000!

AFTER A NUMBER OF FURTHER HOUSE CALLS,...

I--DIDN'T DARE REFUSE PAYING OFF! IT WAS MY MONEY--OR MY LIFE!

THAT MAKES YOU THE TENTH VICTIM! HOLY RACKETS! WE'VE GOT TO FIND A WAY TO CLIP THE WINGS OF KILLER MOTH, BATMAN!

ON THEIR WAY BACK TO THE BATCAVE...

I HAVE A PLAN IN MIND, ROBIN-- BUT WE'LL NEED THE SERVICES OF ALFRED!

THAT'LL PLEASE ALFRED! HE FEELS SO PROUD WHEN WE ASK HIM TO TAKE A HAND IN OUR CASES!

AND IN THE BATCAVE THAT VERY EVENING,...

ALFRED, TAKE THIS BAG TO THE CORNER OF MORTIMER ROAD AND WILSON LANE! I'M SUPPOSED TO DROP OFF $100,000 IN THAT DESERTED AREA--BUT BRUCE WAYNE IS NOT LEAVING THIS HOUSE TILL FURTHER NOTICE!

VERY GOOD, SIR!

NOT LONG AFTER, IN **MOTH MANSION**...

SO! BRUCE WAYNE ADVISES ME HE WON'T PAY! HE'S GOING TO STAY PUT IN HIS HOUSE-- SURROUNDED BY THE POLICE! I WARNED HIM THAT TO TIP OFF THE COPS WOULD MEAN HIS DEATH--

AND THAT'S THE WAY IT'S GONNA BE-- eh, **KILLER**?

LARVA, YOU AND **PUPA** KEEP AN EYE ON WAYNE MANSION! SOONER OR LATER THOSE COPS WILL FINALLY LEAVE! WE'LL MOVE IN WHEN THEY GO! WHAT'LL HAPPEN TO BRUCE WAYNE WILL GUARANTEE US FULL COOPERATION FROM THOSE OTHER MILLIONAIRES STILL ON THE LIST!

NOW BEGINS FOR THE TWO MOTH-MEN A PERIOD OF UN-RELAXING VIGILANCE...

WE'VE BEEN HERE FOR THREE DAYS-- AND HAVEN'T SIGHTED A SINGLE COP! BUT BRUCE WAYNE KEEPS HIM-SELF HOLED UP IN THE HOUSE!

HE WAS BLUFFIN' ABOUT CALL-ING IN THE COPS! IT'S TIME WE REPORTED TO **BOSS-MOTH**!

DURING THESE SAME DREARY DAYS OF WAITING, BARBARA GORDON IS ALSO MARKING TIME. BUT HER **NIGHTS** ARE FILLED WITH ACTIVITY...

¬SIGH¬ I SUPPOSE I'LL NEVER USE IT-- BUT I CAN DREAM... AND THIS NEW **BATGIRL** COS-TUME WILL BE READY... JUST IN CASE...

AFTER HOURS, IN THE BASEMENT STOREROOM OF THE LIBRARY, SHE KEEPS HERSELF IN FIGHTING SHAPE...

I'M STRONGER AND HARDER THAN I'VE EVER BEEN, THANKS TO MY SPECIAL PROTEIN DIET AND INTENSIVE EXERCISE!

BUT--ALAS FOR DREAMS AND EXPECTATIONS OF HIGH ADVENTURE!-- CRASS EVERYDAY ACTIVITIES MUST ALWAYS TAKE PRECEDENCE.

THIS RARE EDITION OF THE **BAY PSALM BOOK** WHICH BRUCE WAYNE HAS BEEN AFTER ME TO GET HIM JUST ARRIVED SPECIAL DELIVERY! HE COLLECTS RARE BOOKS-- AND SOMETIMES MY CONTACTS HELP LOCATE THEM FOR HIM!

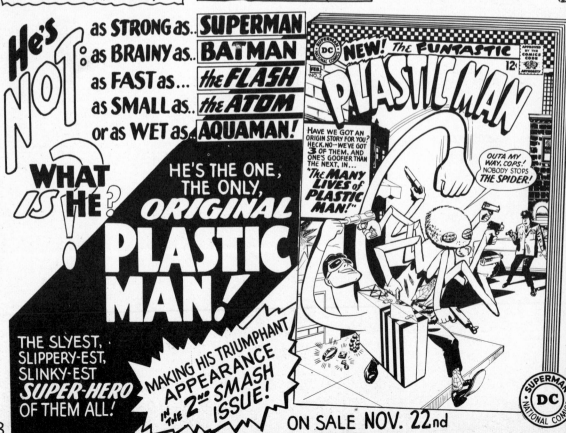

SURGING FURY FILLS THE HEART OF THE LIBRARIAN EVEN AS TEARS BRIM OVER IN HER EYES! SHE HAS WORKED FOR THIS MOMENT WHEN SHE CAN ONCE AGAIN APPEAR AS *BATGIRL* -- BUT NOW ALL THE PLEASURE HAS GONE OUT OF IT!

AS HER HANDS HIT THE ROLLED BRIM OF HER BERET, BRINGING IT DOWN OVER HER FACE AND NECK...

...HER FINGERS PULL AT HER SKIRT -- WHICH REVERSES AND BECOMES A CAPE...

...SHE TOUCHES HER BOOTS, ROLLING UP THEIR FLAPS...

...AND HER HANDBAG REVERSES ITSELF TO FORM HER SPECIALLY-DESIGNED WEAPONS BELT...

THEN THE *NEW* -- THE *REAL* -- *BATGIRL* MAKES HER FIRST APPEARANCE BEFORE THE WORLD -- AND *KILLER MOTH* AND HIS MOTH-MEN...

KILLER MOTH -- NO WONDER YOU PICKED THAT NAME!

BATGIRL AGAIN -- HEYY -- A HORRIBLE THOUGHT JUST HIT ME! DO YOU SUPPOSE *SHE'S* WORKING WITH *BATMAN* THE WAY *ROBIN* DOES?

BATMAN FIST MEETS MOTH-MAN CHIN...

ZOKK

ANOTHER FLYING MOTH-MAN IS GROUNDED BY ROBIN...

THWAKK

BUT-- WHEN A FALLING MOTH-MAN HITS BATGIRL AND KNOCKS HER BACKWARD, OFF BALANCE ...

MMMPPFF!!!

SHHHH!

FURY SHAKES THE BRAVE BEAUTY AS SHE RECOGNIZES HER ASSAILANTS ...

SHE MUST HAVE KNOCKED HERSELF OUT! LET'S CLEAR OUT OF HERE!

AND WHEN THE ECHO OF RACING FEET FADES IN THE AIR ...

WELL!! YOU TWO CERTAINLY WERE A BIG HELP! YOU LET KILLER MOTH GET AWAY! YOU'VE SPOILED EVERYTHING! AND-- AND P-POOR BRUCE WAYNE ...

NO, BATGIRL! WE DIDN'T SPOIL ANYTHING-- YOU DID!!

WHA--WHAT ARE YOU SAYING?

WE PLANNED ALL THIS IN ORDER TO FOLLOW *KILLER MOTH* TO HIS HIDE-OUT--SO WE COULD NOT ONLY CAPTURE HIM BUT ALSO RECOVER THE MILLION DOLLARS HE EXTORTED FROM SOME OF *GOTHAM CITY'S* WEALTHIEST MEN!

BRUCE WAYNE IS SAFE AND SOUND! WITH HIS CO-OPERATION WE RIGGED UP THIS LIFE-LIKE DUMMY TO FOOL THE *MOTH-MEN!* WE DIDN'T KNOW HOW TO GO TO *THEM* SO WE ARRANGED MATTERS SO THEY'D COME TO *US!*

OHHH! I'VE SPOILED EVERY-THING!

AWW, CHEER UP, *BATGIRL!* ALL ISN'T LOST YET! WE CAN STILL GO AFTER *KILLER MOTH!* YOU SEE--I PLANTED A TRACKING DEVICE UNDER THE FENDER OF THE *MOTHMOBILE!*

I'M GOING ALONG WITH YOU--

NO, *BATGIRL!* THIS IS A CASE FOR *BATMAN* AND *ROBIN!* I'M SORRY--BUT YOU MUST UNDERSTAND THAT WE CAN'T WORRY OUR-SELVES ABOUT A GIRL ...

AS THE *BATMOBILE* ROARS OFF, A RAGING YOUNG TIGRESS YANKS A SPECIAL MOTOR BIKE FROM THE TRUNK OF HER SPORTS CAR ...

WORRY ABOUT A GIRL, eh? HAH! IF THEY THINK THEY CAN CUT ME OFF FROM WHERE THE ACTION IS, THEY'RE MISTAKEN! I RESTYLED THIS MOTOR BIKE FOR JUST SUCH AN EMERGENCY!

FAR AHEAD OF THE *BAT-MOBILE,* THE *MOTH-MOBILE* STREAKS TOWARD THE SECURITY OF *MOTH MANSION* ...

BRUCE WAYNE IS DEAD! MY SCHEME WILL BE SURE-FIRE NOW! NO OTHER MILLIONAIRE WILL DARE DEFY ME! WHY-- I MAY EVEN "UP" THE ANTE--DEMAND $200,000!

ON THE DASHBOARD OF THE *BATMOBILE* A TRACKING NEEDLE QUIVERS--TURNS--FOLLOWING THE MOVEMENTS OF THE *MOTHMOBILE...*

WHILE ON THE *BAT-BIKE,* MULTI-COLOR LIGHTS FLARE AND DIM--INDICATING TO THE *MASKED MAIDEN* WHAT ROAD TO FOLLOW IN HER SECRET PURSUIT...

OUTSIDE *MOTH MANSION,* SOON AFTERWARD...

NOW LET'S SINGE THAT *KILLER MOTH* WITH A FEW CHOICE PUNCHES!

IT'LL BE A PLEASURE, I "MOTH" SAY!

FROM ABOVE, KEEN EYES WATCH THE *DYNAMIC DUO* RACE INTO THE LEPIDOPTERAL LAIR...

I CAN'T IMAGINE HOW *BAT-MAN* AND *ROBIN* GOT INVOLVED IN THIS CAPER, BUT I'M READY FOR THEM WITH A TASTE OF MOTH HOSPITALITY!

FEATHERY FINGERS TOUCH SPECIAL CONTROLS AND THE *MASKED MAN-HUNTERS* GO SOARING UPWARD INTO THE AIR...

YEOW! WE-- WE'RE FLOATING! IF WE DON'T GET OUT OF THIS BIND, WE'LL BE LIKE DUCKS IN A BARREL FOR THE *MOTH-MEN!*

THIS MUST BE A GRAVITY-FREE CHAMBER--MAKING US WEIGHTLESS-- THE SAME SORT OF CHAMBER THE ASTRONAUTS USE TO PRACTICE ORBITAL FLIGHTS IN!

UNKNOWN TO THE STRUGGLING CRIME-FIGHTERS, *BATGIRL* IS HOT ON THEIR HEELS...

OHHH! WAIT! I HAVE AN IDEA! DON'T GO 'WAY NOW!

DON'T GO WAY? IS SHE KIDDING!?

RACING BACK TO THE *MOTHMOBILE*, THE RESOURCEFUL GIRL REMOVES THE MAGNETIC TRACKING DEVICE PUT UNDER ITS FENDER BY *ROBIN*.

I'LL TIE THIS MAGNET ABOUT ONE OF MY BOOTS!

MOMENTS LATER...

THE METAL BASEBOARD HEATING STRIP WILL ANCHOR ME SECURELY THROUGH THE MAGNET-- SO GRAB HOLD, *BATMAN!*

HURRY UP! I HEAR THE *MOTH-MEN* COMING TO TAKE POT SHOTS AT US!

SLIDING HER MAGNETIC BOOT ALONG THE BASEBOARD, THE *DOMINOED DARE-DOLL* WHIPS HER ARM ABOUT AND THE WEIGHTLESS *BATMAN* AND *ROBIN* GO FLYING FORWARD...

GO GET 'EM, BOYS!

SAVAGE FISTS ROCK AND SOCK IN UNISON...

WHONK!

THWAK!

TAKE THIS ONE, *ROBIN!*

HE'S "TOOKEN", *BATMAN!*

WOPP!

KRA

NICE DEDUCTION, *BATMAN!* BUT I'LL BET YOU WERE MIGHTY GLAD TO SEE ME WHEN YOU AND *ROBIN* WERE UP IN THE AIR IN THAT GRAVITY-FREE CHAMBER!

WELL--SINCE *YOU* BROUGHT THE SUBJECT UP--I *COULD* HAVE ESCAPED--AND WAS ABOUT TO WHEN YOU APPEARED--BY FIRING MY *LASER TORCH,* USING THE PRINCIPLE OF ACTION AND REACTION TO REACH SAFETY!

IN POLICE HEADQUARTERS, AFTER *KILLER MOTH* AND HIS MOB HAVE BEEN IMPRISONED AND THEIR MILLION DOLLARS EXTORTION MONEY RETURNED TO THE VICTIMS...

LOOKS AS IF YOU HAVE A NEW MEMBER OF THE TEAM, *BATMAN!* OR WILL SHE PROVE TO BE A CRIME-FIGHTING *RIVAL?*

I'LL WELCOME HER AID, COMMISSIONER GORDON--WHEN AND WHERE THE OCCASION ARISES! FROM WHAT I'VE SEEN, SHE DOESN'T HAVE TO TAKE A BACK SEAT TO ANYBODY!

STILL LATER, IN THE GORDON HOME...

THAT *BATGIRL* SURE IS TOPS IN MY BOOK! *HARRUMPH!* TOO BAD *YOU* COULDN'T BE A LITTLE MORE *LIKE* HER, BABS!

IF DAD ONLY KNEW!

The End

WILL THE *NEW* BATGIRL APPEAR AGAIN? THAT DEPENDS ON *YOU,* READERS! WRITE AND LET US KNOW!

⑩

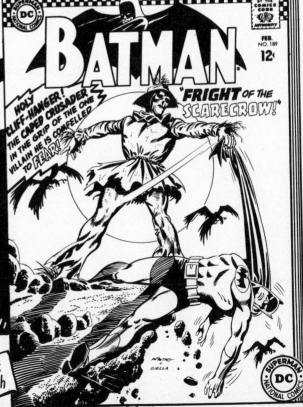

MOMENTS LATER, SIX DARING GENTLEMEN RISE INTO THE INKY SKY...

REMEMBER... THE FIRST TO REACH THE CLIFF ON THE FAR SIDE OF THE RIVER WINS!

HIGHER AND HIGHER THEY RISE! BREEZES SEPARATE THE DANGLING COMPETITORS! ONE, *PEDRO VALDES*, DRIFTS AWAY, AND...

A SOUND... A SOUND OF *WINGS*...!

MOTHER OF GOD! *TRAINED FALCONS*...RIPPING THE BALLOON TO *SHREDS*!

MORE THAN A *HUNDRED FEET* TO THE GROUND! I AM *LOST*!

LIKE A STONE, THE HORRIFIED MEXICAN DROPS... WHEN SUDDENLY, A DARK FIGURE STREAKS FROM THE SHADOWS ...SPEEDS TOWARD THE EDGE OF THE CLIFF!...

IF I CAN HIT HIM *SOLIDLY*... AND *FAST*...

338

2

...I MIGHT BE ABLE TO CARRY HIM PAST THE ROCKS...

AND INTO THE RIVER!

THEN, AS THE STUNNED VALDES REACHES THE SAFETY OF THE NEAR BANK...

THE BATMAN...! ALWAYS I HAVE THOUGHT OF YOU AS AN AMERICAN *LEGEND!* NEVER DID I *DREAM* THAT YOU WOULD SAVE MY LIFE...

...FOR THAT YOU CERTAINLY *DID*...

CARAMBA! HE HAS *VANISHED!* WAS THIS A *MAN*...OR A *WRAITH?!*

SEÑOR VALDES' QUESTION WOULD BE ANSWERED IF HE COULD SEE HIS SAVIOR ASSUMING ANOTHER IDENTITY, THAT OF **BRUCE WAYNE**, THE **GOTHAM CITY** SOCIALITE AND PHILANTHROPIST...

SOMETHING ROTTEN GOING ON HERE...

IT'S OUT OF CHARACTER FOR **MUERTO**... A NOTORIOUS RECLUSE...TO GIVE THIS HUGE PUBLIC FIESTA...

...AND INVITE EVERY SOCIAL BUTTERFLY IN THE WESTERN HEMISPHERE!

BATMAN DIDN'T LEARN MUCH ON HIS BRIEF TOUR OF THE ESTATE...

...EXCEPT THAT SOMEONE IS KEEPING FALCONS TRAINED TO **KILL!**

AH, BRUCE! IT IS A PLEASURE TO HAVE YOU WITH US AGAIN!

DID YOU ENJOY YOUR **WALK?**

YOU HAVE SOME LOVELY LAND, **SEÑOR!** AND A LOVELY **WIFE!**

ONE DOES NOT EXPECT SUCH A **YOUTHFUL** AMERICAN TO BE SO WELL-**MANNERED!**

SHE **CAN'T** BE ANY OLDER THAN I...YET SHE SPEAKS AS THOUGH I WERE A **CHILD!**

YOU ALSO **DANCE** SUPERBLY! WE MUST GET TO KNOW EACH OTHER **BETTER!**

SHE'S YOUNG, VERY BEAUTIFUL... BUT THERE'S A STRANGE FEELING OF **MUSTINESS** ABOUT HER!

I SEE VALDES IS BACK! APPARENTLY HIS DUNKING DIDN'T DO HIM ANY PERMANENT HARM!

WONDER WHY **HE** WAS SINGLED OUT FOR A MURDER ATTEMPT?

FOR NOW, I'D BETTER CONCENTRATE ON BEING CHARMING!

QUITE AN IDEA YOU AND JUAN HAD...! I'VE NEVER BEEN TO A PARTY IN A **GRAVEYARD** BEFORE!

MOST PEOPLE **FEAR** DEATH! JUAN AND I CHOOSE TO **LAUGH** AT IT!

4

GRIMLY, DESPERATELY, THE STRUGGLE CONTINUES... THE MURMUR OF NIGHT BREEZES BROKEN ONLY BY THE PANTING OF THE WOULD-BE ASSASSINS AND THE SOFT STACCATO SOUNDS OF COMBAT...

WHUMP

ABRUPTLY, ANOTHER SOUND... THE SHRILL SCREECH OF A HIGH-PITCHED WHISTLE...

SKA

WEEEEEEEEEP

FIRST, A PADDING OF PAWS OVER THE SUN-SCORCHED EARTH ...A FETID ODOR./ THEN A PAIR OF GIANT WOLVES ANSWERS THE WHISTLED SUMMONS, THEIR EYES GLEAMING WITH KILL-LUST IN THE MOONLIGHT...

6

AS THOUGH SHOT FROM A CANNON, *THE BATMAN* LEAPS UPWARD...

DO NOT AIM TO KILL!

SI! IT IS MUCH BETTER TO MERELY BRING HIM DOWN...

...AND LET THE PETS OF OUR MASTER FINISH THEIR WORK!

BUT BEFORE THE THUGS CAN TRIGGER THEIR RIFLES, *THE BATMAN* ONCE MORE LEAPS...OUT, AWAY FROM THE TREE! FOR A MOMENT, HE SOARS AS GRACEFULLY AS HIS NIGHT-FLYING NAMESAKE...

...THEN PLUNGES OVER THE EDGE OF THE CLIFF AND HURLS TOWARD THE JAGGED STONE FLOOR BELOW!...

I HEARD NO SPLASH!

HE DID NOT HIT THE RIVER! HE MUST BE LYING IN THE SHADOWS...

...AND NO MORTAL COULD SURVIVE THAT DROP! HIS FEAR OF THE WOLVES MUST HAVE BEEN GREAT INDEED!

AT THAT MOMENT, THE MUERTOS ARE CONFERRING IN LOW VOICES...

THOSE BUNGLERS AND THEIR GUNS! THEY HAVE FAILED!

THEN, DEAR HUSBAND, WE MUST ATTEND TO VALDES OURSELVES!

SEÑOR VALDES, YOU APPEAR UNHAPPY! WE HAVE A THING TO SHOW YOU THAT WILL GIVE YOU JOY...

COME! IT IS IN THE OLD MONASTERY!

SO IT IS THAT THE TRIO STROLLS TOWARD THE RUIN, ALONG THE CLIFF-EDGE...

THIS THING YOU WISH ME TO SEE...WOULD IT BE A FLOWER, PERHAPS?

THE SEÑOR IS VERY WISE!

IT WILL PLEASE YOU, SEÑOR VALDES... IT MAY EVEN BE WHAT YOU SEEK!

THE MUERTOS AND THEIR PREY... JUST ABOVE ME!

IT'S DOUBLY FORTUNATE I LEFT MY ROPE HANGING AT THIS PARTICULAR SPOT...

I FIGURED I MIGHT NEED IT TO GET ME TO THE CLIFF BOTTOM IN A HURRY ...BUT I DIDN'T FORESEE THAT IT WOULD SAVE MY LIFE...OR PROVIDE A CONVENIENT LISTENING POST!

8

THEY'RE ENTERING THAT RUINED *MONASTERY*...

I COULD *SHOUT*...WARN VALDES...BUT THEN I'D LOSE MY BEST CHANCE AT LEARNING THE *MUERTOS'* SECRET!

BEHOLD MY TREASURES! LOVELY, ARE THEY NOT?

LOVELY... AND *DANGEROUS!* ACCORDING TO LEGEND, THE *SYBIL FLOWERS* CONFER *IMMORTALITY*...

...BUT AT THE COST OF TOTAL, UTTER *INSANITY!*

DURING YOUR RECENT STAY IN *MEXICO CITY,* YOU MADE A *MISTAKE,* MUERTO...

YOU LEFT ONE OF THE BLOSSOMS IN YOUR HOTEL ROOM! PERSONALLY, I DO NOT *BELIEVE* THE IMMORTALITY NONSENSE...HOWEVER, AS A GOVERNMENT AGENT...

I AM ORDERED TO *ARREST* YOU BOTH!

MY FRIEND...SURELY YOU WOULD NOT ABUSE OUR *HOSPITALITY!* I *IMPLORE* YOU...

GET THAT TORCH AWAY FROM MY *EYES*....!

UNNGH

K-CHOK

CALL US *MAD,* VALDES? YOU *DARE* INSULT US THUS...?

THE MIGHTY ONE FELL *EASILY* TO THE ILLUSION-CREATING POWER OF THE *SYBIL* FLOWERS, EH, MY SWEET?

IT IS NOT SURPRISING! RECALL HOW THE FLOWERS FIRST AFFECTED *US!*

THEY WILL NOT ESCAPE FROM THE VINES WE BOUND THEM WITH! THEY ARE *TENEMOS* VINES...

...THEY RESIST EFFORTS TO PULL THEM LOOSE BY *CONTRACTING* ALL THE MORE!

SHALL WE UNMASK *THE BATMAN?*

NO! LET HIM PERISH IN HIS SECRET GUISE! THIS IS *FITTING!*

AND EVEN *MORE* FITTING WILL BE THE *MANNER* OF HIS DEATH ...A DEATH BY *BIRDS!*

Pᴀɪɴꜰᴜʟ MOMENTS CREEP PAST ON BOOTS OF LEAD... AND *BATMAN* STRUGGLES TO REGAIN CONSCIOUSNESS...

I'M *NOT* SEEING THOSE...SHAPES! I MUST *CONVINCE* MYSELF...IT'S ALL AN *HALLUCINATION!*

FORCE MYSELF TO...*REASON* ...TO *ESCAPE!*

CAN'T *BREAK* MY BONDS... SO I'LL *CUT* THEM! GOT TO *CONCENTRATE* ON UNPINNING VALDES' BADGE...

12

348

SNARING THAT BIRD...IF A BIRD *IS* THERE...WOULD BE TRICKY EVEN WITH FULL USE OF MY FACILITIES...

CHUNK

GOT TO STOP THINKING '...SIMPLY *ACT!* DRAG VALDES...AND MYSELF... AWAY FROM THIS FIENDISH GARDEN...

FRESH AIR... MY HEAD'S CLEARING! EVERY-THING VALDES SAID ABOUT THOSE PALE, PRETTY FLOWERS IS *TRUE*....!

IF EVER THEY WERE CIRCULATED AMONG THE WORLD'S POPULATION, THERE WOULD BE AN EPIDEMIC OF *MADNESS!*

MUERTO LEFT HIS *TORCH*...

...IT WILL SERVE TO BURN...TO *OBLITERATE*... THE *SYBILS!*

JUAN, MY BELOVED HUSBAND... *LOOK!* OUR FLOWERS... OUR *LIFE*... THE ONLY PATCH OF *SYBILS* LEFT...

...OUR *IMMORTALITY* BEING BURNED FROM THE SOIL!

14

STORY:
DENNY O'NEIL

ART:
NEAL ADAMS
& DICK GIORDANO

EDITING:
JULIE SCHWARTZ

The END

DOLORES MUERTO 1843 – 1969

JUAN MUERTO 1840 – 1969

STORY BY: FRANK ROBBINS

MAN OR BAT?

ART BY: NEAL ADAMS & DICK GIORDANO

GOTHAM CITY...IN THE LAB OFFICE OF BIOCHEM, LTD., WHOLESALER OF RARE BIOCHEMICALS...

...WHERE AN INTENT HEIST-GANG WORKS, UNAWARE OF A SILENT WATCHER, HANGING POISED ABOVE THEM...

TIME IS RUNNING OUT FOR ME! WHAT'S TAKING THEM SO BLASTED LONG?

I NEED ONE ITEM IN THAT SAFE MORE THAN *THEY* DO!

S-450

AH-H-H-- THEY'VE CRACKED IT! NOW TO MAKE A GRAND-ENTRANCE LIKE MY IDOL-- THE *BATMAN*-- AND SCARE THEM OF-- EH?!

MY MYSTERIOUS ALLY FROM THE *MUSEUM OF NATURAL HISTORY CAPER* ＊! HE'S COME TO HELP ME *AGAIN!*

NOT THAT I WAS IN REAL TROUBLE, FRIEND-- BUT YOU SURE HELPED MAKE IT SHORT AND SWEET!

SKREEK! IT WAS IN MY OWN SELFISH INTERESTS TO END IT *QUICKLY,* BATMAN--BECAUSE...

＊"CHALLENGE OF THE MAN-BAT!" *in:* DETECTIVE COMICS #400

...THERE'S SOMETHING IN THAT SAFE *I MUST HAVE--FAST!*

HOLD IT! WE JUST FOUGHT TO *PREVENT* A THEFT...AND UNTIL I GET THE POLICE HERE, *NOTHING* IS TOUCHED!

YOU DON'T *UNDERSTAND!* I CAN'T-- *WAIT! NO ONE* STOPS ME...

...NOT EVEN *YOU,* BATMAN!

SKREEK! I'M NO THIEF--LIKE THOSE *RATS! SEE...* I'M PREPARED TO *PAY* FOR WHAT *I* TAKE!

SO YOU ARE! BUT THIS IS *AFTER* BUSINESS HOURS... AND NO WAY TO "BUY" A MEDICAL PRODUCT!

SKREEK--DON'T FORCE ME INTO BEING YOUR-- *ENEMY!* PLEASE...

③ 355

WHILE A MAN IN THE GUISE OF A *BAT*--BUT NEVER IN DANGER OF LOSING HIS HUMAN IDENTITY--COMES TO HIS SENSES.

WHAT TERRIBLE INNER CONFLICT TORTURES THAT-- CREATURE?

HE SAID HE'D PAY FOR WHATEVER HE TOOK! BUT *WHAT* WAS IT?

AND HOW CAN IT *SAVE* HIM?

IS HE A HUMAN BAT-- OR A BAT WITH HUMAN TRAITS?

SPEEDING AWAY AFTER NOTIFYING THE POLICE TO PICK UP THE HEIST GANG...

I ONCE SAID HE'D MAKE A FORMIDABLE *FRIEND*-- OR *FOE*! IS THIS TO BE THE *DECISIVE* HOUR-- WHEN IT CAN GO *EITHER* WAY?

I MUST FIND HIM! PERHAPS IN THE MUSEUM, WHERE I *FIRST* MET HIM?

AT *BATMAN'S* DESTINATION, ANOTHER SEEKS ENTRANCE...

YOU *MUST* LET ME IN! I'M HIS FIANCÉE, FRANCINE LEE--I *MUST* SEE HIM!

I DUNNO, MISS-- HE'S THE *ONLY* ONE PERMITTED IN AFTER HOURS! --EH? *BATMAN*-- HERE?

BATMAN? OH, THANK HEAVEN-- MAYBE *YOU* CAN HELP ME!

PROF. LANGSTROM-- OUR...ER....*BAT*-SPECIALIST! HE'S BUSY PREPARING AN EXHIBIT, AFTER A RUSH TRIP TO *CHICAGO*!

WHO CAN'T SHE SEE?

BUT--THAT'S THE POINT! KIRK *NEVER* WENT TO *CHICAGO*! I PHONED HIS MOTHER! SHE ISN'T *SICK* AT ALL! AND HE HASN'T BEEN HOME HERE, IN DAYS!

HMMM... SOUNDS LIKE AN ELABORATE *COVER-UP*, MISS LEE! AND I'M AFRAID I KNOW *WHY*! COME ON...

6

BUT ALMOST AS IF ON WINGS...

CONTINUING HIS HEADLONG FLIGHT, THE MAN-BAT SEEKS THE SHELTERING GLOOM OF GOTHAM'S CENTRAL PARK!

MY ONLY REFUGE-- MY ONE CHANCE AT NORMALCY-- DESTROYED!

CURSE BATMAN!

HE-HE'S ALIVE! BUT-- HOW CAN YOU BE SO SURE IT-- HE'S--KIRK?

WHEN HE FIRST SAW YOU, HIS VOCAL CORDS FROZE...BUT HIS SAD, CONTORTED MOUTH FORMED ONE WORD THAT I LIP-READ...FRANCIE!"

ONE FINAL CLINCHER CONVINCED ME, FRANCINE!

THIS SYNTHESIZED BIOCHEMICAL--I RECOGNIZE IT! A COUNTER-ACTIVE GRAND STIMULANT-- AND BIOCHEM, LTD. IS THE ONLY SOURCE FOR IT IN THE U.S.A.!

BUT I HAVE THE ESSENTIAL ELEMENTS FOR COMPOUNDING IT--IN MY BATCAVE!

IF I CAN ONLY FIND KIRK IN TIME!

8

ALSO REALIZING HIS IMMEDIATE PERIL, THE *MAN-BAT* FRANTICALLY FLAPS HIS... *ARMS?*

SKREEK! W-WHAT...?

BUT ARE THEY *ONLY* "ARMS" NOW?

SKREE-EEK! BAT-WINGS...?!

THE TRANSFORMATION IS :UGH: *COMPLETE!*

THE FEAR-DRIVEN FOOL! EVEN HIS CAPE WON'T SLOW THAT HEAD-LONG ESCAPE-PLUNGE...

HE'LL HIT THE WATER LIKE A *ROCK!*

BUT NOW--I'M *FREE!* FREE LIKE MY LITTLE "*BROTHER*"...

...WHO WILL NOW SHARE HIS HIDEAWAY WITH *ME!*

:GASP:

KIRK'S MONSTROUS MUTATION IS FINALLY *COMPLETED!* MAYBE EVEN *I* CAN'T SAVE HIM NOW!

WHERE AM I? THIS IS NO ORDINARY CAVE...

SKREEK! THIS COULD ONLY BE-- THE BATMAN'S HOME... THE BATCAVE!

SUDDENLY...*

ARGH-H...!

* OUTSIDE, BATMAN PRESSES THE DASHBOARD BUTTON THAT ACTIVATES THE CAMOUFLAGED CAVE-DOOR... AND THE INSIDE LIGHTS...

GOOD OLD BATCAVE! NEVER THOUGHT I'D BE NEEDING YOU SO SOON! BUT MUST HAVE THAT FORMULA READY-- WHEN THE POLICE GRAB LANGSTROM!

TEMPORARILY BLINDED, A FRANTIC MAN-BAT SEARCHES MADLY FOR HIS ONLY KNOWN ESCAPE ROUTE...

HAS TO BE-- BATMAN RETURNING!

I'VE LOST MY BEARINGS! WHERE IS THAT EXIT?

NOCTURNAL FOOL! I'VE FORGOTTEN MY GREATEST ACQUIRED WEAPON FOR SURVIVAL--SONAR!

12

WHEN I **DON'T** GET A **BOUNCE-BACK**-- I'VE FOUND MY **EXIT**!

SKRE SKREE

EK EEK

SKREEK

MORE BLINDING LIGHTS--BUT **NO ECHO**! I'VE **FOUND** IT!

IT'S--**LANGSTROM**! HIDING HERE...?!

SEEMS **BLINDED**! HE'LL DASH HIMSELF RIGHT INTO MY CAR...!

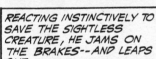

REACTING INSTINCTIVELY TO SAVE THE SIGHTLESS CREATURE, HE JAMS ON THE BRAKES--AND LEAPS OUT...

MUST DIVERT HIM....

BUT THE **MAN-BAT'S** NATURAL SONAR HAS ALREADY WARNED HIM--AND VEERING TO AVOID THE CAR, HE SMASHES INTO THE **NEW** OBSTACLE PUT SUDDENLY IN HIS PATH!...

OOO-F!

STUNNED BY THE MASSIVE IMPACT, BOTH FIGHT TO REGAIN THEIR SENSES--

HE'S STRUGGLING TO FREE HIMSELF-- LIKE A TERRIFIED, CORNERED-- **ANIMAL**!

YARGH-H! SKREEK!

LANGSTROM! LISTEN TO ME-- I'VE COME HERE TO **HELP** YOU!

14

YARK-K!

IN FREE-FALL TO INSTANT DEATH FAR BELOW, THE DESPERATE *BATMAN* CLUTCHES WILDLY ABOUT HIM... AND BREAKS HIS FALL ENOUGH TO...

THOMP

IF HE GETS AWAY NOW--HE'S *DOOMED!* MUST KEEP HIM HERE-- BUT *HOW?*

REMOTE CAR-CONTROL ON BELT! BRING CAR *TO* ME! THEN...

15

IN ALL THIS BLEAK, CAVERNOUS COUNTRYSIDE THERE IS BUT A SINGLE GLEAM OF LIGHT -- A YELLOWED LUMINESCENCE GLOWING IN A CRUMBLING TOWER --

-- AND THEREIN STANDS A LOVELY GIRL, TROUBLED, TERRIFIED --

-- WHILE WITHOUT, AN EERIE FIGURE GLIDES OVER THE TANGLED GROUNDS AS SILENT AS A SHADOW ON SNOW.

NO NOISE, NO MORTAL SOUND BREAKS THE SHROUDED STILLNESS, SAVE THE SCRAPING TOGETHER OF SKELETAL LIMBS IN THE TOPS OF ANCIENT TREES... AND A DISTANT, AGONIZED HOWL THAT MAY BE AN ANIMAL PLEADING FOR THE MOON, OR MAY NOT!

FOLLOW The BATMAN as he plunges into the morass of evil where lurks --

The Demon of Gothos Mansion!

STORY: Denny O'Neil   ART: Irv Novick and Dick Giordano

S-516

© 1970 National Periodical Publications, Inc.

IT BEGAN JUST TWO DAYS AGO, WITH THE ARRIVAL OF A LETTER--

all... to
a... and... sition is yo
and so, dear uncle, while my employer seems gentlemanly, I can't help feeling that something strange is happening here. The house is remote and isolated, and the children I have been hired to tutor seem, to put it mildly, very odd indeed.
I hope you are well. Give my regards to Bruce Wayne and Dick Grayson.
Your loving niece,
Daphne.

INTERESTING MAIL, ALFRED?

INTERESTING-- AND *BIZARRE*, MASTER BRUCE! IT'S A NOTE FROM MY NIECE, DAPHNE -- PERHAPS YOU REMEMBER HER* --THE ACTRESS?

*NOTE: AND *YOU* REMEMBER HER, READER OF OURS, IF YOU THRILLED TO HER FIRST APPEARANCE IN "ANGEL--OR DEVIL" *BATMAN* #216! -- Editor.

SHE HAS BEEN...ER... *AT LIBERTY* THESE PAST FEW MONTHS! SHE ACCEPTED A POSITION AS *TEACHER* FROM A *MR. CLIFTON HEATHROW*...

BUT HERE, SIR--READ IT YOURSELF!

UMMM... THE DEAL *DOES* SEEM *UNUSUAL*!

I SUPPOSE THERE'S NO CAUSE FOR *WORRY*! STILL --

-- STILL, YOU'D LIKE *THE BATMAN* TO CHECK!

--AND I *AGREE*!

THUS IT IS THAT THE *CAPED CRUSADER* STANDS ON A BARREN ESTATE IN THE MOUNTAINS A HUNDRED MILES FROM THE NEAREST TOWN--

THOSE FELLOWS APPEAR TO BE *GUARDS!* I COULD EVADE THEM--*EASILY!*

--BUT I'M *CURIOUS...*

...*WHY* WOULD ANYONE POST WATCH-MEN *HERE?* I'LL TEST THEIR *HOSTILITY*-- BY *SHOWING* MYSELF!

GOOD EVENING, GENTLEMEN! BIT *NIPPY* FOR THIS TIME OF YEAR, ISN'T IT?

EH--? WHO BE THAT?

--'TIS A GIANT *BAT!*

NONSENSE YOU TALK, *EPHRAIM!* 'TIS NO MORE THAN A *MAN!* STRIKE A *FLAME*--WE'LL HAVE A *LOOK* AT HIM!

FEEL *FREE!* MIND TELLING ME THE NAME OF THIS PLACE?

GOTHOS MANSION-- AND WE'VE NO LIKING FOR *STRANGERS!*

WELL, NOW THAT YOU'VE SEEN ME, I'LL BE STROLLING ON!

BUT NOT *FAR*--!

WHEN THEY SAID THEY DIDN'T LIKE *STRANGERS* --THEY WEREN'T *KIDDING!*

FORTUNATELY, I WAS *PREPARED* FOR A SNEAK ATTACK!

FOR LONG YEARS, THIS **BATMAN** HAS TRAINED--AND **OTHER** MEN, ARMED THOUGH THEY BE, ARE NO MATCH FOR HIM...

SWIFTLY, NOISELESSLY, *THE BATMAN* CROSSES THE GROUNDS, AND...

SOMEONE'S COMING--! I MAY LEARN MORE *UNSEEN...*

WHEN WE POSITION THE ALTAR, ALL WILL BE IN READINESS, *ELDER HEATHROW!*

EXCELLENT, EXCELLENT! BE *MERRY,* FELLOWS OF THE *COVEN OF GOTHOS MANSION--*

--TONIGHT, FOR THE FIRST TIME IN *TWO CENTURIES,* WE RAISE THE SPIRIT OF THE DEMON *BALLK--*

THE TRIO CONTINUES THROUGH THE UNDERBRUSH, LEAVING ONLY A FAINT SMELL OF MUSK IN THE CHILL NIGHT AIR--

DAPHNE HAS STUMBLED INTO TROUBLE -- THE *WORST KIND!* A *COVEN* IS A GROUP DEDICATED TO *BLACK MAGIC--*

--AND I RECALL THAT *BALLK* IS ONE OF THE *NASTIEST* CREATURES IN MYTHOLOGY!

ELDER HEATHROW IS APPARENTLY THE CHIEF *WARLOCK--* AND OBVIOUSLY *MAD--*

--WHICH DOESN'T MAKE HIM ANY LESS *DANGEROUS!*

THERE'S ONLY *ONE* WINDOW LIT IN THE HOUSE!

SO THAT'S WHERE I BEGIN LOOKING FOR DAPHNE!

ALMOST AS THOUGH HE WERE WEIGHTLESS, *THE BATMAN* RISES UP THE SMOOTH, STONE TOWER...

PLEASE... *PLEASE*, MISTER HEATHROW-- LET ME *OUT*!

YOU HAVE NO CAUSE FOR FEAR, MISS PENNYWORTH!

THE-- BATMAN--!!

I'VE COME TO TAKE YOU AWAY FROM HERE, DAPHNE!

THANK *HEAVEN*!-- IT'S BEEN *HORRID*! THEY MADE ME WEAR THESE AWFUL, OLD CLOTHES... THEY'VE KEPT ME LOCKED UP...

...AND THE CHILDREN I WAS HIRED TO TEACH... I DISCOVERED THEY'RE NOT *REALLY* KIDS--THEY'RE A PAIR OF HIDEOUS *DWARVES*!

6

AHH... *THE BATMAN!* MY SENTRIES *WARNED* ME YOU WERE ABOUT!

KINDLY DO NOT STRUGGLE! MY PISTOLS ARE *AGED*, BUT IN *EXCELLENT* CONDITION!

YOU SHALL DIE-- *EXQUISITELY!*

TIMOS...CYNBEE... PREPARE OUR VISITOR FOR HIS FATE! BIND HIS HANDS--

AYE, ELDER! 'TIS DONE!

THEN...

I SHALL EXPLAIN! THIS DEVICE WAS ORIGINALLY BUILT BY MY GREAT-GREAT-GRANDFATHER TO PUNISH DISOBEDIENT SERVANTS!

THE BLOCK UPON WHICH YOU STAND IS FIXED TO WEIGHTS UNDER THE FLOOR--

--CLEVERLY CONTRIVED TO *DROP* SLOWLY INTO THE CELLAR!

IN A QUARTER OF AN HOUR OR SO, THE NOOSE AROUND YOUR NECK WILL BEAR YOUR FULL WEIGHT...HANGING YOU, OF COURSE!

WHILE YOU'RE AT IT, EXPLAIN *MORE!* WHAT DO YOU WANT WITH MISS PENNYWORTH?

FOR *YEARS*, I SEARCHED FOR A MAIDEN BORN PRECISELY AT *MIDNIGHT* ON *OCTOBER 31ST* ... A MINUTE EITHER WAY WOULD NOT HAVE SUFFICED!

FOR IF SUCH A ONE IS *SACRIFICED* THIS NIGHT, THE SPIRIT OF *BALLK* WILL ARISE ONCE MORE!

SIX GENERATIONS MY FAMILY HAS LIVED TO DO THIS DEED!

AND MISS PENNYWORTH FULFILLS YOUR CONDITIONS?

YOU REALIZE, YOU'RE *MAD*?!

NOT AT ALL! MY ANCESTOR ACTUALLY *SUCCEEDED* IN LIBERATING THE DEMON!

THE GHOST OF THE MAIDEN THEN SLAIN STILL WALKS THESE VERY HALLS!

AND NOW -- *FAREWELL*!

ALREADY... HARD TO BREATHE! I WON'T *LAST* FIFTEEN MINUTES!

TOES BARELY TOUCHING THE PLATFORM BUT THERE *IS* A CHANCE... A SLIM ONCE...

THAT *TORCH*! IF I CAN TENSE MY NECK MUSCLES... KEEP FROM STRANGLING...

9

...START MYSELF *SWINGING* FORWARD...

...NOW *BACKWARD*...

...TO GATHER ENOUGH MOMENTUM...

...TO REACH IT...

MADE IT! NOW TO TWIST AROUND!

GOTTA GET MY HANDS LOOSE...

BURNS LIKE THE DEVIL...BUT BETTER *BURNS* THAN *DEATH*!

10

NEED A MOMENT ...TO CATCH MY BREATH!

YOU MUST NOT TARRY! THE RITES OF BALLK HAVE BEGUN!

DAPHNE! YOU ESCAPED!

I AM... NOT DAPHNE PENNYWORTH! BUT I WILL LEAD YOU TO HER!

THE COVEN HOLDS ITS UNSPEAKABLE CEREMONY IN THE OLD CHAPEL! THIS WAY... HURRY!

HER VOICE... SO ODDLY HOLLOW-- LIKE AN ECHO!

AND HER TOUCH... LIGHT AS A WHISPER! BUT-- FIRM!

THAT NEAR-HANGING MUST'VE DONE THINGS TO MY MIND--

...BECAUSE I DON'T EVEN KNOW HER NAME-- AND YET I'M FILLED WITH AN OVER-WHELMING FEELING OF... LOVE!

THERE LIES THE CHAPEL ... THE COVEN PRANCES WITHIN! I CAN TAKE YOU NO FURTHER!

YOURS IS A HOLY MISSION-- FOR THE ELDER IS A PIT OF EVIL!

GO!

HEAR US, O *BALLK*...UNTO YOU I GIVE THIS MAIDEN, THAT ONCE MORE YOU MAY STAND AMONGST US!

THERE COMES A COLD GUST OF WIND, AND A FETID ODOR OF DECAY SWEEPS OVER THE CONGREGATION--! THE TORCHES DIM TO A FAINT GLOW, AND FOR A CHILL INSTANT, BLACKNESS CLAIMS ALL...

A WAVERING FIGURE SEEMS TO SWELL FROM THE DARK, AND THE ODOR BECOMES A CHOKING STENCH --

THEN, THE FLAMES SPURT TO FULL BRIGHTNESS AGAIN, AND...

THE CEREMONY IS *OVER*, ELDER! YOUR *BALLK* WILL REMAIN IN WHATEVER HELL SPAWNED HIM!

NO! THE DEMON *MUST* BE SERVED--!

PUT THAT PITCHFORK *DOWN!*

SERVANTS OF BALLK --AID ME!

THE RAGGED MEMBERS OF THE INSANE MOB SURGE FORWARD, A TERRIBLE MALICE SMEARED UPON THEIR FACES! IN A SINGLE SWEEPING MOTION, *THE BATMAN* LIFTS THE ELDER--

--AND FLINGS HIM ...

DEMORALIZED, FEARING FOR THEIR LIVES, THE *COVEN* FRAGMENTS AND FLEES--

DON'T LEAVE ME...

I AM ALONE... DESERTED BY ALL!

AND *YOU*, BALLK-- HAVE YOU *ALSO* DESERTED ME--?

THEN... I *DIE*....!

14

HIS HEART COULDN'T TAKE IT, I GUESS!

POOR TWISTED SOUL...

YOU'LL BE ALL RIGHT, DAPHNE! THE DANGER IS PAST--FOREVER!

GO TO THE MANSION! I'LL JOIN YOU THERE, AS SOON AS... I SEE SOMEONE!

HIS BLOOD POUNDING, *THE BATMAN* RUNS OUT OF THE CHAPEL, HIS EYES STRAINING UNTIL HE SEES THE WOMAN HE SEEKS... AND A PURE JOY CATCHES HIS VOICE AS HE CALLS TO HER...

COME... COME TO ME...

I CAN *NOT*, THOUGH, I WISH WITH ALL MY HEART I COULD...

IN BESTING THE *COVEN,* YOU HAVE *FREED* ME!

FARE THEE WELL, *BATMAN...*

WAIT... MY LOVE...

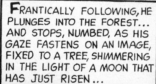

FRANTICALLY FOLLOWING, HE PLUNGES INTO THE FOREST... AND STOPS, NUMBED, AS HIS GAZE FASTENS ON AN IMAGE, FIXED TO A TREE, SHIMMERING IN THE LIGHT OF A MOON THAT HAS JUST RISEN...

End

AND THE NIGHT IS QUIET...

BIBLIOGRAPHY

COMIC BOOKS

All-Star Comics
  (cameo appearance)
  #7 (Oct.–Nov. 1941)
  (guest appearance)
  #36 (Aug.–Sept. 1947)

Batman Comics
  From #1 (Sept. 1940)

Batman Miniatures
  6 issues
  1966

Batman Three-D
  #1
  1953, repeated in 1966

The Brave and the Bold
  #28 (March 1960) (with the Justice League); through # 30 (July 1960)
  #59, #64, #67–71, #74 on (1964–1971)

80 Page Giant
  #5 (Dec. 1964)
  #12 (July 1965)
  #15 (Oct. 1965) (with Superman)

Detective Comics
  From #27 (May 1939)

Giant Batman Annual
  7 Issues
  1961—Summer 1964

Jerry Lewis Comics
  #97
  Dec. 1966

Justice League of America
  From #1
  Oct.—Nov. 1960

New York World's Fair
  #2 (with Robin)
  1940

Star-Spangled Comics
  #65 (Feb. 1947)
  #30 (July 1952)
  (Robin solos but Batman appears frequently)

SUPERMAN MAGAZINES

  Batman appears frequently in:
  Superman Comics
  Lois Lane
  Jimmy Olsen

World's Best
  #1
  Sept. 1941

World's Finest
  #32 (Summer 1941) through #197 (Oct.—Nov. 1970)
  #198, 199 (cameo)
  #202 (May 1971)
  #207 (Nov. 1971)

OTHER MEDIA IN WHICH
BATMAN APPEARED

Batman
    Animated Cartoons
    CBS Network
    Fall 1968—Fall 1970

Batman
    Movie Serial
    Columbia Pictures
    1956–1957

Batman
    A Signet paperback book
    March 1966

Batman
    Movie Serial
    Columbia
    1943

"Batman"
    Television Program
    1966

Batman and Robin
    Movie Serial
    Columbia
    Late 1940s

*Batman and the Fearsome
Foursome*
    Full-length movie
    Twentieth Century-Fox
    1966
    Novelized version
    Signet
    1966

*Batman Versus Three Villains
of Doom*
    A Novel
    By Winston Lyon
    Signet
    1966

Batman Versus *the Joker*
    A Signet paperback book
    May 1966

Batman Versus *the Penguin*
    A Signet paperback book
    May 1966

"Superman Radio Show"
    Batman made frequent appear-
    ances in the mid-1940s

Syndicated Newspaper Strip
    1943–1945
    1966–1971—Ledger Syndicate

Paths into Poetry

by **Joanne Collie** *and* **Gillian Porter Ladousse**

Oxford University Press

Oxford University Press
Walton Street, Oxford OX2 6DP

Oxford New York Toronto Madrid Delhi Bombay
Calcutta Madras Karachi Kuala Lumpur
Singapore Hong Kong Nairobi Dar es Salaam
Cape Town Melbourne Auckland

and associated companies in
Berlin Ibadan

Oxford and *Oxford English*
are trade marks of Oxford University Press

ISBN 0 19 421716 7
© Oxford University Press 1991
Second impression 1992

Typeset by Wyvern Typesetting Limited, Bristol
Printed in Hong Kong